Exercises and Projects for
for

A Programming Approach

The
Little SAS®
Book

a   p r i m e r

SIXTH   EDITION

Rebecca A. Ottesen
Lora D. Delwiche
Susan J. Slaughter

The correct bibliographic citation for this manual is as follows: Ottesen, Rebecca A., Lora D. Delwiche, and Susan J. Slaughter. 2020. *Exercises and Projects for The Little SAS® Book, Sixth Edition.* Cary, NC: SAS Institute Inc.

Exercises and Projects for The Little SAS® Book, Sixth Edition

ISBN 978-1-64295-617-7 (Hard cover)
ISBN 978-1-64295-284-1 (Paperback)
ISBN 978-1-64295-524-8 (Web PDF)
ISBN 978-1-64295-525-5 (epub)
ISBN 978-1-64295-526-2 (Kindle)

SAS Institute Inc., SAS Campus Drive, Cary, NC 27513-2414

January 2020

Contents

About This Book

Who should use this book This book was written for anyone who wants hands-on experience while learning or practicing the basics of SAS programming. The exercises and projects in this book are designed so that they can be used in a classroom setting or by an individual reader working alone.

Content This book consists of exercises (with selected solutions) and projects. Each chapter in this book covers the same material as the corresponding chapter in *The Little SAS Book, Sixth Edition*. The content in each chapter builds on previous chapters, so we do not expect a reader to use a technique in one chapter that is introduced in a later chapter.

> **Exercises** There are three types of exercises in this book: multiple choice, short answer, and programming. Each type of exercise is designed to improve the comprehension of topics and syntax, and to develop SAS coding skills with realistic data sets.

> **Solutions** Solutions are provided for odd-numbered multiple choice and short answer questions. Solutions are not provided for programming exercises, but hints are provided to help give readers direction.

> **Projects** The projects in the final chapter are designed to serve as a comprehensive capstone for the programming skills developed throughout the book. Each project gives readers a chance to synthesize the material learned from various chapters. Completing a project will take several days of intense thought and coding, and will result in a final product that could serve as evidence of SAS proficiency to a future employer or course instructor. Projects can be completed by a group or an individual.

Typographical Conventions This book uses the same typographical conventions as *The Little SAS Book*. SAS doesn't care whether your programs are written in uppercase or lowercase, so you can write your programs any way you want. In this book, we have used uppercase and lowercase to tell you something. All SAS keywords appear in uppercase letters. A keyword is an instruction to SAS and must be spelled correctly. Anything that programmers make up such as variable names, names for SAS data sets, comments, or titles are generally shown in lowercase or mixed-case letters.

Data Sets We have tried to include programming exercises with data sets that are somewhat large, unruly, and messy. We hope that this will help our readers develop their skills more fully. Some of the exercises are based on data that come directly from public sources, while others have been designed to mimic real-life scenarios.

The data sets for exercises can be accessed via web pages for any of the authors of this book at the support site for SAS, support.sas.com/publishing/authors (select the name of the author;

then, look for the cover thumbnail of this book and select Exercise Data). The data sets are organized by chapter, and they are also available in a single, downloadable ZIP file. If you are unable to access the data through the website, send an email to saspress@sas.com.

The projects in the final chapter use real data. We give instructions for locating and downloading the data from primary sources so that you will have the most up-to-date and authentic data possible.

How to use this book The exercises are organized in such a way as to help readers develop useful and sensible programming habits. Readers are encouraged to examine all raw data files and SAS data sets they will be accessing before writing any code.

In many of the programming exercises, we do not explicitly ask the reader to use a particular function or procedure. This was intentional in order to provide users with the opportunity to develop code based on what they learned from the topics that are covered in the corresponding chapter. This means that the code written by one person may not be the same as that written by another person, even though they both may arrive at the same answer.

While the material presented in the book includes exercises for certain graphical and statistical analyses, the purpose of these chapters is merely to introduce the basic syntax and concepts, and not the fine details of the analysis itself. This book may be used in a statistics course as a programming supplement. However, it should not be considered a statistical textbook.

Compatibility with SAS software This book was developed using SAS 9.4, but the exercises are compatible with SAS 9.3 and later. Most exercises require only Base SAS, but a few in Chapter 9 require SAS/STAT, and a few in Chapters 2 and 10 require SAS/ACCESS Interface to PC Files. The exercises in this book were designed to be programmed in the SAS windowing environment, SAS Enterprise Guide, SAS Studio, SAS OnDemand for Academics, or the SAS University Edition through SAS Analytics U. We have noted the few instances when an exercise is specific to the SAS windowing environment. Otherwise, the exercise can be considered environment-independent. Path references in this book are, however, specific to Microsoft Windows, and may need to be adjusted for other environments such as UNIX, Linux, or z/OS. (SAS University Edition runs in a Linux environment even if you are using a Windows PC.)

For Instructors Instructors may obtain a complete solutions manual by completing the form found at the "Instructors Solutions" link on the web pages for any of the authors at support.sas.com/publishing/authors, and providing the appropriate credentials. The solutions given for the programming exercises are not the only ones possible. Many of the exercises can be solved in multiple ways. Instructors may choose to share a snippet of output or a graph if they think their students need a little extra help to complete an exercise. The section references that accompany the instructors' solutions refer to the sections in *The Little SAS Book, Sixth Edition* where the material is covered. These references are listed only for the corresponding chapter of the exercise even though the answer may use subject matter from a previous chapter.

We encourage instructors to add their own follow-up questions to any of the exercises for class assignments. In Chapter 9, "Using Basic Statistical Procedures," we have supplied many extra variables in the data sets so that instructors can append additional questions according to the content covered in their course.

For the projects in the final chapter, instructors may choose to download and distribute the data for the class to use. Instructors may clean the data for the class as they see fit, or leave the data manipulation to the students instead.

Additional Help   Although this book illustrates many programming tasks and analyses regularly performed in businesses across industries, questions specific to your aims and issues may arise. To fully support you, SAS Institute and SAS Press offer you the following resources:

- For questions about topics covered in this book, contact the authors through SAS Press at saspress@sas.com.

- For questions about topics in or beyond the scope of this book, post queries to the relevant SAS Support Communities at communities.sas.com.

- To search the SAS user Knowledge Base or contact SAS Customer Support you can visit support.sas.com.

About The Authors

 **Rebecca A. Ottesen** first learned SAS as a student at California Polytechnic State University, San Luis Obispo, where she now teaches for the Statistics Department. As a biostatistician for the City of Hope, Rebecca uses every opportunity to incorporate her research and programming experience into the coursework for her Cal Poly students.

 **Lora D. Delwiche** enjoys teaching people about SAS software and likes solving challenging problems using SAS. She has spent most of her career at the University of California, Davis, using SAS in support of teaching and research.

 **Susan J. Slaughter** discovered SAS software in graduate school at North Carolina State University. Since then, she has used SAS in a variety of business and academic settings managing large databases, teaching SAS software classes, and helping other SAS programmers. She now works as a consultant through her company, Avocet Solutions.

Learn more about these authors by visiting their author pages, where you can download free book excerpts, access example data, read the latest reviews, get updates, and more:

support.sas.com/ottesen
support.sas.com/delwiche
support.sas.com/slaughter

Acknowledgments

1. Which of the following is true about the technical reviewers, editors, designer, technical publishing specialist, and marketing specialist for this book?
   a. They are smart
   b. They are hard-working
   c. They are wonderful
   d. All of the above

The correct answer is D! We are grateful to have had the support of so many insightful people who contributed to this book. Our reviewers (Marie Boman-Davis, Hunter Glanz, Lynette Harris, Laura Kapitula, Isabel Litton, Sanjay Matange, Lelia McConnell, Sandy Owens, and Christine Wells) provided us with invaluable feedback and perspective that helped us shape this book so that it will develop important skills for beginning programmers. Robert Harris, our cover designer, made all of our cover ideas come to life. Our technical publishing specialist, Denise Jones, ensured that the final version of the book looked great. To Sian Roberts, our marketing specialist, thank you for helping to promote our book and getting the word out. We offer a special thank you to Catherine Connolly, our developmental editor and copyeditor, for hanging in there and standing by our side every step of the way. And, finally, this book would also not have been possible without the support of our families, friends, loyal readers, and students (you know who you are), thank you.

CHAPTER 1

Getting Started Using SAS Software

Multiple Choice

1. Which of the following is not a comment in SAS?

    a.   `/* I am not a comment */`
    b.   `* I am not a comment ;`
    c.   `/* * I am not a comment; */`
    d.   All of the above are valid comments

2. What other term is appropriate for referring to a SAS data set?

    a.   A column
    b.   A row
    c.   A table
    d.   None of the above

3. Which of the following is a valid variable name when using the VALIDVARNAME=V7 option?

    a.   AbCdEfGhIjKlMnOpQrStUvWxYz
    b.   %Change
    c.   Debt-Ratio
    d.   1stProcedure

4. In SAS data sets, missing numeric data are represented by which of the following?

    a. A single space
    b. A single period
    c. Any number of spaces
    d. Any of the above

5. What is the main difference in the naming convention for SAS data libraries versus SAS variables?

    a. SAS data library names can contain special characters such as $, % and #
    b. Variable names are case sensitive
    c. SAS data library names can only be up to 8 characters long
    d. Variable names can contain underscores

6. What is a SAS data library?

    a. A location where SAS data sets are stored
    b. A location where the SAS log messages are stored
    c. A location where SAS procedure results are stored
    d. All of the above

7. How many SAS statements does this program contain?

    ```
    DATA instock; INFILE supply;
       INPUT Brand $
             Model $
             Quantity;
    RUN;

    PROC PRINT DATA = instock;
    RUN;
    ```

    a. 2
    b. 3
    c. 6
    d. 7

8. Which statement does not indicate the end of a DATA or PROC step?

    a. STOP
    b. QUIT
    c. END
    d. RUN

9. By default, SAS will execute the DATA step one time each for which of the following?

    a. Variable
    b. Observation
    c. Data set
    d. Procedure

10. Which of the following is not an interactive environment for editing and submitting SAS programs?

    a. SAS windowing environment
    b. SAS Studio
    c. SAS Enterprise Guide
    d. Batch mode

11. What will the value of F be in the data set called TEMPS?

    ```
    DATA temps;
      F = (C * 9/5) + 32;
      C = 0;
    RUN;
    ```

    a. .
    b. 0
    c. 32
    d. 34

12. In the SAS windowing environment, you can edit SAS data sets by using which of the following?

    a. Results Viewer
    b. Output window
    c. Results window
    d. Viewtable window

13. If a program does not run correctly, where can you find the error messages?

    a. The end of the program
    b. The log
    c. The results
    d. The output

14. When you submit a SAS program in an interactive environment, which window or tab will always show activity?

    a. Enhanced Editor
    b. Log
    c. Results
    d. Output

15. Which of the following is true about OPTIONS statements?

    a. They are specified in DATA steps
    b. They are global
    c. These statements modify your default settings for future SAS sessions
    d. The first OPTIONS statement in a program overrides subsequent ones

16. Suppose you submit the following code. Any output formatted for printing that is created after this statement will have what characteristics?

    ```
    OPTIONS NUMBER NOCENTER;
    ```

    a. Left-justified with no page numbers and no date
    b. Left-justified with no page numbers with today's date
    c. Left-justified with page numbers and no date
    d. Left-justified with page numbers with today's date

Short Answer

17. Would the layout of the following PROC PRINT code cause SAS to produce an error? Explain why or why not, and rewrite the code so that it is more organized.

    ```
    PROC
            PRINT
    DATA = new;        RUN;
    ```

18. SAS ignores anything inside a comment. Explain why it is a good idea to add comments to your program.

19. Suppose that you need to record information on the annual salary of employees as a variable in a SAS data set. Would it be better to store this information as a character or numeric variable? Explain your choice.

20. A coworker tells you, "SAS programs always start with a DATA step." Is this true? Explain why or why not.

21. Explain why SAS data sets are self-documenting.

22. Which will occur first: execution of the last statement in the DATA step or reading of the last observation in an input data set? Explain your choice.

23. Explain in what order SAS processes observations in a DATA step.

24. Explain why it is a good idea to check your SAS log.

25. Describe what a global statement is and identify two such statements.

26. Explain why using the OPTIONS statement is the most flexible way to specify a system option.

Programming Exercises

27. The body mass index (BMI) is a measure used as a rough indicator of an individual's body fat. The following program computes BMI using weight (in pounds) and height (in inches).

```
** Compute Body Mass Index using pounds and
   inches;
DATA bodymass;
   Gender = 'Male';
   Weight = 150;
   Height = 68;
   BMI = (Weight / Height ** 2) * 703;
RUN;
```

   a. Type this program into the editor and submit it.
   b. This program creates a SAS data set named BODYMASS in the WORK library. View the data set. Find the value that was calculated for the BMI variable and record this value as a comment in your program.
   c. View the properties of the data set to identify the type of each variable and record them as comments in your program. How you view the properties varies depending on what SAS interface you are using.
   d. Choose different values for the variables Weight and Height in your program. Add a PROC PRINT to list the data in the BODYMASS data set and submit the revised program.

28. SAS system options control many aspects of the way SAS runs. You can list the current values of system options using the OPTIONS procedure. You can change the value of system options using the OPTIONS statement.

    a.   Write a program that contains the OPTIONS procedure, and submit it.
    b.   In your SAS log, find the following options: MISSING=, OBS=, PAPERSIZE=, and YEARCUTOFF=. Add comments to your program stating the current values of these options.
    c.   Using an OPTIONS statement, change the option CENTER to NOCENTER. Then add another PROC OPTIONS to your program and submit the new SAS statements. Check your log to confirm that the option has been changed to NOCENTER.

29. The following DATA step attempts to create a SAS data set that contains information about a city.

```
OPTIONS NONUMBR;

DATA info;
   City = 'Sao Paulo';
   Country = 'Brazil'
   CountryCode = 55;
   CityCode = 11;
RUN;
```

    a.   Type this program into SAS and submit it. Review the information in the SAS log. In a comment in your program, identify the number of notes, warnings, and errors produced by this code (not including any start-up messages).
    b.   Revise the code to fix the programming mistakes, and then resubmit it.
    c.   Review the information in the SAS log. In a comment in your program, identify how many observations and variables were created in this data set.

CHAPTER 2

Accessing Your Data

Multiple Choice

1. What type of data files are not considered raw data?

    a. ASCII files
    b. CSV files
    c. Text files
    d. SQL tables

2. In the SAS windowing environment, the Viewtable window is useful for which of the following actions?

    a. Combining existing SAS data sets
    b. Entering data into a SAS data set
    c. Exporting data to another file type
    d. Importing data from another file type

3. Which of the following is a valid libref name that can be used to create a permanent SAS data set?

    a. working
    b. 365days
    c. permanent
    d. All of the above

4. Which DATA statement will create a permanent SAS data set called DOGS assuming that all SAS libraries have been properly defined?

    a. `DATA dogs.sas7bdat;`
    b. `DATA dogs;`
    c. `DATA sasdata.dogs;`
    d. None of the above

5. When using the following direct reference to create a permanent SAS data set in the Windows operating environment, what does the name *dogs* refer to?

    `DATA 'c:\MySASLib\dogs';`

    a. The drive
    b. The directory
    c. The filename
    d. The libref

6. The descriptor portion of a SAS data set includes which of the following?

    a. The SAS engine with which the data set was created
    b. The date on which the data set was created
    c. The number of variables and observations
    d. All of the above

7. Which optional statement in PROC IMPORT tells SAS to expect a column that contains both character and numeric values?

    a. GETNAMES = NO
    b. GETNAMES = YES
    c. MIXED = NO
    d. MIXED = YES

8. Which PROC IMPORT option identifies the type of Microsoft Excel file to be read?

    a. DELIMITER=
    b. DBMS=
    c. DATAROWS=
    d. None of the above

9. If your raw data file contains only data and no variable names, which PROC IMPORT option should you use?

    a.   DELIMITER=
    b.   GUESSINGROWS=
    c.   GETNAMES=
    d.   OUT=

10. The data in the following program are an example of what type of data?

```
DATA readme;
   INPUT Place $ Code $;
   DATALINES;
AG 5678
SLO 1234
PB 3456
   ;
RUN;
```

    a.   Character
    b.   Instream
    c.   Internal raw data
    d.   All of the above

11. Which statement is synonymous with a DATALINES statement?

    a.   DATA
    b.   INFILE
    c.   CARDS
    d.   INPUT

12. Which SAS statement enables you to refer to an external raw data file?

    a.   DATALINES
    b.   DATA
    c.   INFILE
    d.   INPUT

13. Which of the following types of data cannot be read with list input?

    a.   Missing data indicated by a period
    b.   Date and time values
    c.   Standard numeric data
    d.   All of the above

14. Assuming that the raw data are arranged in neat columns, what is an advantage of column input?

    a. It can read missing data indicated by spaces
    b. It can read embedded blanks
    c. It can read character data longer than eight characters
    d. All of the above

15. With column input, you cannot do which of the following?

    a. Read data separated by spaces
    b. Specify an informat in the INPUT statement
    c. Read numeric data in scientific notation
    d. All of the above

16. Given this note in the SAS log, what could you add to fix the INPUT statement so that the ID variable would be read correctly including all digits and hyphens?

    ```
    INPUT ID GPA Age;

    NOTE: Invalid data for ID in line 1 1-9.
    RULE:      ----+----1----+----2
    1          5437-2212 3.84 21
    ID=. GPA=3.84 Age=21 _ERROR_=1 _N_=1
    ```

    a. A dollar sign
    b. A column range
    c. An informat
    d. None of the above

17. Which of the following data values would not require an informat?

    a. 44.5E2
    b. $1,689
    c. 08/18/1920
    d. 4,928

18. Which informat would be appropriate to read the value 07/04/1776?

    a. MMDDYY8.
    b. MMDDYY10.
    c. DATE8.
    d. DATE10.

19. Which input style is the best for reading date values from raw data?

    a. List
    b. Column
    c. Formatted
    d. All input styles can read date values

20. Select the INPUT statement that would be appropriate for reading data values for the variables Name, Salary, and Age in the following raw data.

    ```
    ----+----1----+----2----+----3
    Sally     $64,350 41
    Marian    $55,500 38
    Oprah     $75,000,000 59
    ```

    a. INPUT Name $ Salary & DOLLAR11. Age;
    b. INPUT Name $ Salary :DOLLAR11. Age;
    c. INPUT Name $ @10 Salary DOLLAR11. Age;
    d. INPUT Name $ @'$' Salary Age;

21. Which of the following tells SAS to go to the next line when reading in data?

    a. @
    b. @@
    c. /
    d. +n

22. Which input style can be used with a double trailing @?

    a. Column
    b. List
    c. Both can be used
    d. Neither can be used

23. A record that is being held by a trailing @ will be released for which of the following reasons?

    a. The current loop through the DATA step completes
    b. SAS finds a subsequent INPUT statement with no line-hold specifier
    c. Both of these
    d. Neither of these

24. A record that is being held by a double trailing @ will be released for which of the following reasons?

    a. The current loop through the DATA step completes
    b. SAS finds a subsequent INPUT statement with no line-hold specifier
    c. Both of these
    d. Neither of these

25. Which of the following is a valid INFILE option that tells SAS to stop reading after the fifth line of raw data?

    a. FIRSTOBS = 5
    b. OBS = 5
    c. TOTALOBS = 5
    d. N = 5

26. Select the INFILE option that specifies that the raw data use a comma as the delimiter.

    a. DLM = ','
    b. DLM = ,
    c. DLM = COMMA
    d. DLM = COMMA.

Short Answer

27. Discuss the advantages of using LIBNAME statements versus direct referencing for creating permanent SAS data sets.

28. Suppose that you inherit a program that reads data from the raw data file called NationalParks.dat into a permanent SAS data set called NATIONALPARKS. Would this cause SAS to overwrite the original raw data file?

29. Explain the reasons that you might choose to use internal versus external raw data.

30. Explain the difference between using a LIBNAME statement versus using an INFILE statement.

31. List five examples of data values that cannot be read with list input.

32. Write an INPUT statement for the following raw data with variables named Year, City, Name1, and Name2.

```
----+----1----+----2----+----3----+----4
18 San Diego       Rebecca Marian
19 San Francisco Kathy   Ginger
20 Long Beach      Scott   Sally
21 Las Vegas       Cynthia MaryAnne
22 San Jose        Ethan   Frank
```

33. In the preceding data set some of the values for the variable City are longer than 8 characters. Explain why using a LENGTH statement with list input is not sufficient to read City correctly for this data set.

34. Describe one advantage of using formatted input over column input.

35. Write an INPUT statement for the following raw data with variables named Brand, Qty, and Amount.

```
----+----1----+----2----+----3
Pampers             42 $44.99
Huggies              7 $34.99
Seventh Generation 7 $39.99
Nature Babycare      4 $41.99
```

36. Explain why it would be a good idea to use an informat when reading data using the & modifier.

37. When reading raw data files, by default, the colon modifier cannot read character data with embedded blanks. Explain why and suggest a type of raw data file that would allow SAS to read embedded blanks using a colon modifier.

38. Examine the following raw data that contain the genus, species, and quantity of plants at a local nursery. Would a line pointer work to read this data file into SAS? Explain why or why not.

```
----+----1----+----2----+----3
Rosa
  multiflora    49
  canina        38
Narcissus
  papyraceus    15
Dendrobium
  kingianum      8
  nobile         5
  phalaenopsis 12
```

39. Examine the following raw data, which contain a patient ID and group designation (A, B, or C) with multiple observations per line. Write the SAS statements that will read the data into variables named ID and Group using a line-hold specifier, and then keep only those patients in groups A and C.

    ```
    ----+----1----+----2----+----3
    4165 A 2255 B 3312 C 5689 C
    1287 A 5454 A 6672 C 8521 B
    8936 C 5764 B
    ```

40. Suppose that you have a raw data file from a national bank that contains millions of transactions from branches across the country. Reading in the entire data set takes too much processing time, and you are only interested in the records that correspond to your branch. Discuss how you can modify the following DATA step to decrease the processing time while reading this raw data file.

    ```
    DATA transaction;
       INFILE 'c:\MyRawData\BankTrans.csv' DLM = ',';
       INPUT Branch_Name Branch_ID Trans_ID Account
             Date MMDDYY8. Start_Time TIME8.
             End_Time TIME8. Amount Balance;
    RUN;
    ```

41. Explain the difference between the TRUNCOVER and MISSOVER options for the INFILE statement.

42. Suppose that you have a raw data file that contains data values with embedded commas and uses tabs as a delimiter. Explain why it would or would not be necessary to enclose the data values in quotes and use the DSD option.

43. Write an INFILE statement that will tell SAS to read the raw data file c:\MyRawData\Records.csv, which contains data values that are separated by commas, and allows for missing data at the end of the record.

Programming Exercises

44. Annual attendance for the top 10 amusement parks in North America is listed in the raw data file ParkAttendance.dat. For each park, the data include the ranking, park name, location, and four years of attendance.

    a. Open the raw data file ParkAttendance.dat in a simple editor such as WordPad. In a comment in your program, state the number of variables and observations.
    b. Use the IMPORT procedure to read the raw data file into SAS. View the log to verify that your data set has the same number of variables and observations as you stated in part a).
    c. Print the data set.

45. The file CancerRates.dat contains data on the top 10 cancer sites in the United States from the Centers for Disease Control and Prevention (CDC) website. These statistics are condensed across genders and races. The variables are ranking, cancer site, and incidence rate per 100,000 people.

    a. Open the raw data file CancerRates.dat in a simple editor such as WordPad. In a comment in your program, state the number of variables and observations.
    b. Read the raw data file into SAS. View the log to verify that your data set has the same number of variables and observations as you stated in part a).
    c. Print the data set.
    d. Copy the CancerRates.dat data set to a different location such as your desktop or a flash drive and read it into SAS a second time from that new location.

46. The American Kennel Club (AKC) reports rankings of dog breeds by year based on the number of registrations. These data are found in the raw data file AKCbreeds.dat. For each breed, the data include the name of the breed, and ranking for each of four years. Breeds with missing ranks were not recognized by the AKC during that year.

    a. Open the raw data file AKCbreeds.dat in a simple editor such as WordPad. In a comment in your program, state the number of variables and observations.
    b. Read the raw data file into SAS. View the log to verify that your data set has the same number of variables and observations as you stated in part a).
    c. Print the data set.

47. The World Health Organization (WHO) monitors vaccine recommendations in countries around the world. The raw data file Vaccines.dat contains the recommended vaccines for a sample of 13 countries. The variables in this file are vaccine name, mode of disease transmission, worldwide incidence, worldwide deaths, and recommendations (stored in 13 individual columns for the respective countries of Chile, Cuba, United States, United Kingdom, Finland, Germany, Saudi Arabia, Ethiopia, Botswana, India, Australia, China, and Japan).

    a. Open the raw data file Vaccines.dat in a simple editor such as WordPad. In a comment in your program, state the number of variables and observations.
    b. Read the raw data file into SAS. View the log to verify that your data set has the same number of variables and observations as you stated in part a).
    c. Print the data set.

48. Each year, *Forbes* magazine publishes a list of the world's 100 biggest companies. Each company receives a score using four metrics: sales, profits, assets, and market value. The final overall ranking is based on a composite score of these metrics. The variables in the raw data file BigCompanies.dat are ranking, company name, country, sales (billions), profits (billions), assets (billions), and market value (billions).

    a. Open the raw data file BigCompanies.dat in a simple editor such as WordPad. In a comment in your program, state which variables must be read in as character and which variables should be read in as numeric.
    b. Read the raw data file into SAS.
    c. Print the data set.

49. Crayola crayons were introduced in 1903, and since then numerous standard colors have been released. Each crayon has a unique name, which corresponds to a hexadecimal code and RGB triplet. The raw data file Crayons.dat contains information on these standard crayon colors with variables corresponding to crayon number, color name, hexadecimal code, RGB triplet, pack size, year issued, and year retired.

    a. Open the raw data file Crayons.dat in a simple editor such as WordPad. In a comment in your program, state which variables must be read in as character and which variables should be read in as numeric.
    b. Read the raw data file into a permanent SAS data set.
    c. Print the data set.

50. The tallest mountains in the world are located in central and southern Asia. The raw data file Mountains.dat contains information on mountains over 7,200 meters (23,622 ft). Researchers measure the prominence of a mountain as the height above the highest saddle connecting it to a higher summit. The variables in this file are mountain name, height (m), height (ft), year of first ascent, and prominence (m).

    a. Open the raw data file Mountains.dat in a simple editor such as WordPad. In a comment in your program, state which variables must be read in as character and which variables should be read in as numeric.
    b. Read the raw data file into SAS.
    c. Print the data set.

51. Information Technology Services (ITS) at Central State University has a computing service called "the Grid," which is offered to faculty, staff, and students. This supercomputer is a cluster of 10 computers that, if programmed correctly in a grid environment, can process much faster by distributing the work across 10 machines. University users that would like to use the Grid computing environment must register with ITS. The raw data file CompUsers.dat contains the variables user ID, classification group (faculty, staff, or student), first name, last name, email address, campus phone number, and department.

    a. Examine the raw data file CompUsers.dat and read it into SAS.
    b. Print the data set.
    c. Write another DATA step to read the raw data file and remove the student records. Do this as efficiently as possible by testing the classification group as it is being read in with the INPUT statement.
    d. Print the data set.

52. The World Health Organization (WHO) collected data in countries across the world regarding the outbreak of swine flu cases and deaths in 2009. The data in the file SwineFlu2009.dat include counts per country by month during the epidemic. There are many variables in the raw data file with the following descriptions:

    By date, ID for sorting by first case date

    By continent, ID (X.YY) for sorting by first case date within a continent where X represents continent X, and YY represents the YYth country with the next first case

    Country

    Date of first case reported

    Number of cumulative cases reported on the first day of the month for April, May, June, July, and August (across the columns, respectively)

    Last reported cumulative number of cases reported to WHO as of August 9, 2009

    By date, ID for sorting by first death date

    By continent, ID (X.YY) for sorting by first death date within a continent where X represents continent X, and YY represents the YYth country with the next first death

    Date of first death

    Number of cumulative deaths reported on the first day of the month for May, June, July, August, September, October, November, and December (across the columns, respectively)

    a. Examine the raw data file SwineFlu2009.dat and read it into SAS.
    b. Print a report that describes the contents of the data set including attributes of the variables.

53.   The data in the file BenAndJerrys.dat represent various ice cream flavors and their nutritional information. The variables in the raw data file are flavor name, portion size (g), calories, calories from fat, fat (g), saturated fat (g), trans fat (g), cholesterol (mg), sodium (mg), total carbohydrate (g), dietary fiber (g), sugars (g), protein (g), year introduced, year retired, content description, and notes.

    a.   Examine the raw data file BenAndJerrys.dat and read it into SAS using a DATA step.
    b.   Read the raw data file using PROC IMPORT.
    c.   Create reports that describe the contents for each data set.
    d.   Note any differences between the two data sets as a comment in your program.

54.   Data on previous winners of the Oscars are stored in a Microsoft Excel file named Oscars.xlsx. The variables in this file are ID, year, host, best picture, best actor, best actress, best director, and best screenplay.

    a.   Examine the Microsoft Excel file Oscars.xlsx and read it into a permanent SAS data set using the IMPORT procedure.
    b.   Print a report that describes the contents of the data set including the attributes of the variables and data set.
    c.   In a comment in your program, discuss any limitations of the functionality of the resulting data set.
    d.   Print the Oscars.xlsx data file using the XLSX LIBNAME engine. In a comment in your program, discuss any limitations of using this method to read in the data.

55.   Researchers randomly assigned subjects to either a treatment group taking a cholesterol-lowering medication daily, or a control group taking a placebo daily. The difference in total cholesterol was measured after four months. The variables in the Tchol.dat file are subject ID, treatment group, difference in cholesterol, pre-treatment total cholesterol, and post-treatment total cholesterol.

    a.   Examine the raw data file Tchol.dat and read it into SAS.
    b.   Print the data set.
    c.   Create a new DATA step and read in the data for only the subjects assigned to the treatment group. Do this as efficiently as possible by testing the treatment group variable as it is being read in with the INPUT statement.
    d.   Print the data set.

56. A gourmet pizza restaurant is considering adding new toppings to its menu. Each month they survey 10 customers about their preferences for three different toppings. They want data on several different toppings, so they don't always ask about the same three toppings. Customers rate each topping on a scale of 1 (would never order) to 5 (would order often). The restaurant wants to compute average ratings for all toppings, so the ratings variables need to be numeric. The raw data file Pizza.csv has variables for the respondent's survey number, and the ratings for five different toppings: arugula, pine nuts, roasted butternut squash, shrimp, and grilled eggplant. The first two digits in the survey number correspond to the month of the survey.

   a. Examine the raw data file Pizza.csv and read it into SAS using the IMPORT procedure.
   b. Print the data set.
   c. Print a report that describes the contents of the data set to make sure all the variables are the correct type.
   d. Open the raw data file in a simple editor like WordPad and compare the data values to the output from parts b) and c) to make sure that they were read correctly into SAS. In a comment in your program, identify any problems with the SAS data set that cannot be resolved using the IMPORT procedure.
   e. Read the same raw data file, Pizza.csv, this time using a DATA step. Be sure to resolve any issues identified in part d).
   f. Print the data set.

57. The Microsoft Excel file named CarTalk.xlsx contains information regarding episodes of the automotive repair radio talk show *Car Talk*. Variables in this file include episode number, air date, title, and a description of the show.

   a. Examine the Microsoft Excel file Cartalk.xlsx by printing the Excel spreadsheet using the XLSX LIBNAME engine.
   b. Read the Microsoft Excel file Cartalk.xlsx into a SAS data set using the XLSX LIBNAME engine.
   c. Read the Microsoft Excel file into a SAS data set using PROC IMPORT.
   d. Print the two SAS data sets.
   e. Read the rows of the Excel file that correspond to the month of May into SAS using the IMPORT procedure. Print the data set.

CHAPTER 3

Working with Your Data

Multiple Choice

1. Which DATA step will not overwrite a temporary SAS data set called TOYS?

    a. `DATA WORK.toys; SET WORK.toys; RUN;`
    b. `DATA 'c:\MySASLib\toys'; SET 'c:\MySASLib\toys'; RUN;`
    c. `DATA toys; SET toys; RUN;`
    d. None of the above

2. Which SAS statement can be used to read a SAS data set?

    a. SET
    b. INFILE
    c. INPUT
    d. All of the above

3. Which of the following assignment statements is valid for the numeric variable Score?

    a. `Score / 100;`
    b. `Score = Score / 100;`
    c. `Score = 'Score' / 100;`
    d. `Score = 'Score / 100';`

4. Given the following raw data and program, what will be the value of Total1 for the second observation in the resulting SAS data set?

```
----+----1----+----2
1  160 50   20
2  150 55   .
3  120 40   30
4  140 50   25

DATA cholesterol;
   INFILE 'c:\MyRawData\Patients.dat';
   INPUT ID Ldl Hdl Vldl;
   Total1 = Ldl + Hdl + Vldl;
RUN;
```

   a. 230
   b. 205
   c. .
   d. 215

5. Given the following raw data and program, what will be the value of Total2 for the second observation in the resulting SAS data set?

```
----+----1----+----2
1  160 50   20
2  150 55   .
3  120 40   30
4  140 50   25

DATA cholesterol;
   INFILE 'c:\MyRawData\Patients.dat';
   INPUT ID Ldl Hdl Vldl;
   Total2 = SUM(Ldl,Hdl,Vldl);
RUN;
```

   a. 230
   b. 205
   c. .
   d. 215

6. Which function can be used to replace text?

   a. TRIM
   b. INDEX
   c. TRANWRD
   d. PROPCASE

7. Which of the following is a valid function for finding the average of X1, X2, and X3?

    a.   AVERAGE(X1,X2,X3)
    b.   AVG(X1,X2,X3)
    c.   MEAN(X1,X2,X3)
    d.   MU(X1,X2,X3)

8. What will SAS return for the value of X?

    ```
    X = MIN(SUM(1,2,3),56/8,N(8));
    ```

    a.   1
    b.   6
    c.   8
    d.   .

9. Which of the following IF-THEN statements will not assign a value of 1 to the variable named Flag for patients with an eye color of blue or brown?

    a.   `IF EyeColor = 'blue' OR 'brown' THEN Flag = 1;`
    b.   `IF EyeColor = 'blue' OR EyeColor = 'brown' THEN Flag = 1;`
    c.   `IF EyeColor IN ('blue','brown') THEN Flag = 1;`
    d.   All of the above will work

10. Which set of IF-THEN/ELSE statements will run without errors?

    a.   ```
    IF 0 <= Age <= 50 THEN Group = 'A';
      ELSE 50 < Age <=70 THEN Group = 'B';
      ELSE Age > 70 THEN Group = 'C';
    ```
    b.   ```
    IF 0 <= Age <= 50 THEN Group = 'A';
      ELSE IF 50 < Age <= 70 THEN Group = 'B';
      ELSE Age > 70 THEN Group = 'C';
    ```
    c.   ```
    IF 0 <= Age <= 50 THEN Group = 'A';
      ELSE IF 50 < Age <= 70 THEN Group = 'B';
      ELSE IF Age > 70 THEN Group = 'C';
    ```
    d.   All of the above will work
    ```

11. Given the following raw data and program, how many observations will be in the resulting SAS data set?

```
----+----1----+----2
41   25 male
32   79 female
36   52 female
74   63 male

DATA pts;
   INFILE 'c:\MyRawData\Measures.dat';
   INPUT ID Age Gender $;
   IF Age < 75;
   IF Age < 50 AND Gender = 'female' THEN
        Guideline = 'Inv4a';
     ELSE IF Age >= 50 AND Gender = 'female' THEN
        Guideline = 'Inv4b';
     ELSE Guideline = 'n/a';
RUN;
```

   a. 1
   b. 2
   c. 3
   d. 4

12. How many clauses are in the following SQL step?

```
PROC SQL;
   SELECT Name, Address, Phone, Email
   FROM contacts;
QUIT;
```

   a. 1
   b. 2
   c. 3
   d. 4

13. When creating a table using PROC SQL, which of the following clauses would select only rows that have a value greater than 10 for the column called Age?

   a. WHERE Age > 10
   b. IF Age > 10
   c. SELECT Age > 10
   d. None of the above

14. Given the following program and SAS data set ANIMALS, what will be the value of the variable DogYears for the second observation in the resulting SAS data set called DOGS?

    ANIMALS

Name	Type	Breed	Age
Mina	Canine	German Shepherd	5
Bailey	Feline	Norwegian Forest	9
Sammy	Canine	Shetland Sheepdog	10
Taco	Canine	Terrier	14

    ```
    DATA dogs;
       SET animals;
       DogYears = Age * 7;
       IF Type = 'Canine' THEN OUTPUT;
    RUN;
    ```

    a. .
    b. 35
    c. 63
    d. 70

15. How many observations will be produced with the following program?

    ```
    DATA new;
       DO p = 1 TO 5;
          OUTPUT;
       END;
    RUN;
    ```

    a. 0
    b. 1
    c. 5
    d. 6

16. Suppose that the YEARCUTOFF= option is set to 1950, and your raw data file has the following date that is read using the MMDDYY8. informat and then printed using the MMDDYY10. format. How would the resulting date appear in the output?

    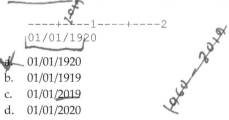

    ```
    ----+----1----+----2
    01/01/1920
    ```

    a. 01/01/1920
    b. 01/01/1919
    c. 01/01/2019
    d. 01/01/2020

17. What is the SAS date value that corresponds to December 25, 1959?

    a. -25
    b. -7
    c. 25
    d. 359

18. What will be the value of Quarter in the following statement?

    ```
    Quarter = QTR(MDY(04,05,2063));
    ```

    a. 1
    b. 2
    c. 3
    d. 4

19. Which type of DATA step statement can be used to initialize a variable to a specified value?

    a. sum
    b. RETAIN
    c. Both of the above
    d. Neither of the above

20. Which of the following is considered a sum statement in the DATA step?

    a. X = A + B;
    b. X = SUM(A,B);
    c. A + B;
    d. All of the above

21. The raw data file called Class.dat contains three test scores for each of two students in a class. If you submit the following SAS program, what will be the value of the variable represented by p(i) for the first observation after the second time through the iterative DO group?

```
----+----1----+----2----+----3
222 Jimmy 95   85   75
333 Ulric 90   80   70

DATA score;
   INFILE 'c:\MyRawData\Class.dat';
   INPUT ID Name $ Test1 Test2 Test3;
   ARRAY t(3) Test1 - Test3;
   ARRAY p(3) Prop1 - Prop3;
   DO i = 1 TO 3;
      p(i) = t(i) / 100;
   END;
   Total = SUM(Test1 - Test3);
RUN;
```

   a.   0.85
   b.   0.80
   c.   0.75
   d.   0.70

22. Referring to the preceding raw data and SAS program, what will be the value of Total for the second observation?

   a.   255
   b.   240
   c.   160
   d.   20

Short Answer

23. Discuss a situation where it would not be a good idea to overwrite a permanent SAS data set by specifying the same name in the DATA and SET statements.

24. Describe why you would not use a SET statement and an INFILE statement to refer to the same data in a DATA step.

25. Explain why the following assignment statement is incorrect for creating a numeric variable X that has a missing value.

```
X = '.';
```

26. Is there a difference between calculating the mean of three variables using a function compared to calculating the mean using an assignment statement as shown in the following code? Explain your answer.

```
Avg1 = MEAN(X1,X2,X3);
Avg2 = (X1 + X2 + X3) / 3;
```

27. Would there be any advantage to using the UPCASE, LOWCASE, or PROPCASE functions when working with messy character data? Explain your answer.

28. An elementary school is holding a public fun run for children and adults as a fundraiser. Runners will start at different times based on age, and must be at least four years old. The following code classifies runners into three groups. Rewrite the code so that once a runner is assigned to a group, SAS will skip the rest of the statements. In addition, make sure that anyone who does not fit into one of the age groups or has a missing value for age is assigned to a fourth group of entrants who require follow-up.

```
** Assign runners to groups 1-3 based on age;
IF 4 <= Age < 9 THEN Group = 1;
IF 9 <= Age < 13 THEN Group = 2;
IF Age >= 13 THEN Group = 3;
```

29. The following portion of code was used to classify patients into stroke risk groups based on their smoking status and blood pressure measurements. Rewrite the code so that it is less repetitive and will keep SAS from checking every condition for every observation. In addition, make sure that patients who fall into more than one group, based on their systolic blood pressure and diastolic blood pressure, will be placed in the group with the highest risk. Add code that will create an unknown risk group for patients with any data that do not fall into the specified ranges.

```
** for smokers;
IF Smoke > 0 AND (0 < Sbp < 120 AND 0 < Dbp < 80)
   THEN Risk = 'Medium';
IF Smoke > 0 AND (120 <= Sbp < 140 OR
                   80 <= Dbp < 90)
   THEN Risk = 'High';
IF Smoke > 0 AND (Sbp >= 140 OR Dbp >= 90)
   THEN Risk = 'Severe';

** for non-smokers;
IF Smoke = 0 AND (0 < Sbp < 120 AND 0 < Dbp < 80)
   THEN Risk = 'Low';
IF Smoke = 0 AND (120 <= Sbp < 140 OR
                   80 <= Dbp < 90)
   THEN Risk = 'Medium';
IF Smoke = 0 AND (Sbp >= 140 OR Dbp >= 90)
   THEN Risk = 'High';
```

30. Suppose that you have an extremely large data set that contains banking transaction records for branches across the United States, with the majority of records coming from the northeastern states. Your task is to group the records into regions based on the state where the transaction occurred. Discuss how you can accomplish this grouping as efficiently as possible.

31. Describe one potential pitfall of using an ELSE statement instead of an ELSE IF statement.

32. How could the following code be rewritten so that it is more efficient? Explain why this might be important with a very large data set and then rewrite the DATA step.

```
DATA mtn;
  INFILE 'c:\MyRawData\UnitedStates.dat';
  INPUT State $ Pop2000 Pop2010;
  IF State IN ('Arizona','Colorado','Idaho',
               'Montana','Nevada',
               'New Mexico','Utah','Wyoming')
  THEN Region = 'Mountain';
  PopDiff = Pop2010 - Pop2000;
  IF Region = 'Mountain';
RUN;
```

33. In the following code, the observations will have a value of missing for the variable HeightCM. Explain why, and how to fix this problem.

```
DATA femaleheight;
  SET height;
  IF Gender = 'Female' THEN OUTPUT;
  HeightCM = HeightIN * 2.54;
RUN;
```

34. In the following code, the data for the 7th, 14th, 21st, and 28th observations in the DETAIL data set are very similar to the resulting observations in the SUMMARY data set. Explain any differences for these observations between the two data sets and why these differences occur.

```
DATA summary detail;
  DO Weeks = 1 TO 4;
    DO Days = 1 TO 7;
      Count + 1;
      OUTPUT detail;
    END;
    OUTPUT summary;
  END;
RUN;
```

35. Explain the difference between a DO statement and an iterative DO statement.

36. In the following code, you were expecting the data set TALLY to have 10 observations, but instead no observations were written. Explain why, and how to fix this problem.

    ```
    DATA tally;
       Sum = 0;
       DO WHILE (Sum >= 10);
          Sum + 1;
          OUTPUT;
       END;
    RUN;
    ```

37. Explain why it is useful to use a date format when working with SAS dates.

38. Suppose a patient database includes the variables DoB (date of birth) and DoNV (date of next visit). Write statements to calculate a patient's current age, age at next visit, and age 90 days after the next visit, reported in years as a whole number.

39. Describe the differences and similarities between a RETAIN statement and a sum statement.

40. Discuss why it is logical that arrays can only contain data of one type, either all numeric or all character.

Programming Exercises

41. Sports Utility Vehicle drivers from across the United States were randomly selected to participate in a study of mileage and gasoline use. Each driver was asked to track the city and highway mileage of their vehicle for seven consecutive days. The SAS data set called GASMILEAGE includes data about the make and model of the vehicle, advertised gas mileage, and seven day driving mileage.

    a. Examine the names, labels, and attributes of the variables in the SAS data set GASMILEAGE. Create a data set that subsets these data to the state you live in (or the state of your choice).
    b. Calculate the average daily city miles driven by each driver during the test week and round this variable to one decimal place. Repeat this for average highway miles.
    c. Use the total mileage recorded during the test week and the corresponding advertised mileage for the vehicle to calculate the total combined number of gallons consumed in the city and on the highway.
    d. Calculate the cost during the test week by using the total gallons consumed and the current average price of regular gasoline for the state you chose in part a). Round this variable to two decimal places.
    e. Using the cost that you calculated, estimate the number of weeks that it will take each driver to spend $1,000 on gasoline.

f. View the resulting data set. In a comment in your program, find the first observation and state the plate ID, average city and highway mileage, cost, and number of weeks to spend $1000.

42. The new management of a local hotel decided to update their recently acquired (and very outdated) property by installing wireless internet service for their guests. They are also considering updating their billing system because the method used by the previous owner seems faulty. In order to conduct a billing analysis, they would like some calculations about the guests who stayed with them during the first part of February (this was the first month after the change of ownership). The raw data file Hotel.txt contains variables with information on room number, number of guests, check-in month, day, year, check-out month, day, year, use of wireless internet service, number of days of internet use, room type, and room rate.

    a. Examine the raw data file Hotel.txt and read it into SAS.
    b. Create date variables for the check-in and check-out dates, and format them to display as readable dates.
    c. Create a variable that calculates the subtotal as the room rate times the number of days in the stay, plus a per person rate ($10 per day for each person beyond one guest), plus an internet service fee ($9.95 for a one-time activation and $4.95 per day of use).
    d. Use PROC SQL to create a variable that calculates the grand total as the subtotal plus sales tax at 7.75%. The result should be rounded to two decimal places. Limit the results to data for room 211 only. In a comment in your program, state the value for the grand total for this room.

43. A local company has recently updated human resources information on their employees from a paper-based system into an actual database where the data can be manipulated and reviewed more efficiently. The raw data file Employees.dat contains information on employees including a de-identified Social Security number, name, date of birth, pay grade, monthly salary, and job title.

    a. Examine the raw data file Employees.dat and read it into SAS.
    b. Modify the appearance of the date of birth variable so that it can be viewed as mm/dd/yyyy.
    c. Suppose that the company conducts their annual review in December. Calculate the age of each employee as of the last day of the current year, and report it in years as a whole number.

d. Using the following information, create variables for the minimum and the maximum annual pay that each employee can receive.

```
Grade    Minimum          Maximum
GR20     $50,000.00       $70,000.00
GR21     $55,000.00       $75,000.00
GR22     $60,000.00       $85,000.00
GR23     $70,000.00       $100,000.00
GR24     $80,000.00       $120,000.00
GR25     $100,000.00      $150,000.00
GR26     $120,000.00      $200,000.00
```

e. For each employee, calculate the expected annual salary for the next year assuming that they receive a 2.5% cost of living increase in January. The result should be rounded to two decimal places. Be sure to also cap the expected annual salary at the maximum amount for the pay grade.

f. Create a bonus variable of $1,000.00 for employees who are leads, managers, or directors, and $0 otherwise.

g. Use PROC SQL to view the resulting data set for William Stone and Mark Harrison. In a comment in your program, state the values for the expected annual salary and bonus for these employees.

44. A regional SAS conference will be held in a few weeks' time. The SAS data set CONFERENCE contains information about the registered attendees and their participation at this event.

a. Review the names, labels, and attributes of the variables in the SAS data set CONFERENCE. Record the label and variable type for Rate as a comment in your program.

b. Using the following registration rates, create a variable that groups attendees as Early, Regular, or On-Site.

```
Academic Early     $295
Student Early      $150
Early              $395
Academic Regular   $350
Student Regular    $200
Regular            $450
On-Site            $550
```

c. Create a variable that represents the participant's area code using the business phone number first. If the business phone number is missing the area code, then use the mobile phone number. If the mobile phone number is missing the area code, then use the home phone number.

d.   The catering committee has already ordered food that does not contain nuts or shellfish, and all meals are kosher, but they need to figure out how many attendees need the special vegetarian or vegan meal. Create a variable that flags the attendees that require a vegan or vegetarian meal as a 1, and as a 0 otherwise.

e.   Use PROC SQL to view the resulting data set for Tina Gonzales (attendee ID 1082) and Patrick Anderson (attendee ID 1083). In a comment in your program, state the values for the registration grouping, participant area code, and special meal flag for these attendees.

45.   The Rose Bowl is a college football tradition that dates back to the early 1900s. The Microsoft Excel file RoseBowl.xlsx contains records on the winning and losing teams during the Rose Bowl's history. The variables in this file are game date, winning team, winning score, losing team, and losing score. These data are sorted by winning team and then by date.

a.   Examine the Microsoft Excel file RoseBowl.xlsx and read it into SAS.
b.   Create a variable that calculates the difference in points between the two teams.
c.   Present the game date using a format that includes the day of the week.
d.   Create a cumulative counter variable that tracks the total number of Rose Bowl games.
e.   Create another cumulative counter variable that tracks the number of wins for each team.
f.   View the entire resulting data set. In a comment in your program, state the values for the game date and score difference of the first Rose Bowl won by the team from Southern California.

46.   A local gym runs a New Year's membership offer that is available to anyone who joins the gym on January 1st. The promotion states that if the new member continues to work out for at least 30 minutes a day for the first four months of the year, then they will have the $150 start-up fee refunded. This year, 245 people signed up for the offer. Members were tracked automatically via the computer check-in system when they arrived and left the gym. The raw data file NewYears.dat contains variables for the member ID, and check-in times for the first 119 days of the year, followed by the check-out times for the first 119 days of the year.

a.   Examine the raw data file NewYears.dat and read it into SAS. Preserve the special characters found in the first row of the data file in the variable names.
b.   Create new variables for the time (in minutes) that the member spent at the gym each day.
c.   Create a flag that identifies whether members are eligible for the refund. Members are eligible if they worked out for at least 30 minutes a day for all 119 days.
d.   Calculate the overall average time spent at the gym for each new member.
e.   Use PROC SQL to view the variables for member ID, refund eligibility, and overall average time for members 330 and 331 in the resulting data set. In a comment in your program, state these values.

47. The data in the file BenAndJerrys.csv represent various ice cream flavors and their nutritional information. The variables are flavor name, portion size (g), calories, calories from fat, fat (g), saturated fat (g), trans fat (g), cholesterol (mg), sodium (mg), total carbohydrate (g), dietary fiber (g), sugars (g), protein (g), year introduced, year retired, content description, and notes.

    a. Examine the raw data file BenAndJerrys.csv and read it into SAS.
    b. Subset the data keeping only flavors that can be purchased at the grocery store (in other words not retired flavors and not Scoop Shop Exclusives as described in the notes variable).
    c. Create a variable that calculates the calories in one tablespoon (TB) of ice cream. Assume that 1 TB = 15 g. Subset the data again keeping only flavors that have this information.
    d. Calculate the total calories you would consume if you were to eat one TB of each flavor of ice cream. Your final total for this variable should appear in the row of the last observation.
    e. Create a variable that identifies the highest number of calories in any one flavor. The result for this variable will appear in the row of the last observation.
    f. View the entire resulting data set. In a comment in your program, state the final values for total calories consumed and the highest number of calories.

48. A study on weight loss in males was conducted over a five-month period. Participants came to a clinic at the beginning of each month, and their weight as well as their responses to six survey questions regarding weight loss were obtained. The raw data file WLSurveys.dat contains variables for subject ID, height (in), weight (lb) at each of five visits, and responses to questions 1-6 at each of five visits. Note that the first six survey responses are from visit one, the next six survey responses are from visit two, and so on, for a total of 30 survey responses.

    a. Examine the raw data file data WLSurveys.dat and read it into SAS.
    b. The survey questions were measured on a scale of 0 (least) to 3 (most). However, the data were recorded inconsistently by data entry clerks; and questions 2, 3, and 5 (for every visit) were accidentally recorded in the reverse order (0 = most and 3 = least). Convert questions 2, 3, and 5 for every visit so that they are measured in the same direction as the other questions.
    c. Missing data were recorded as -99. Reclassify these values as a period (.) to signify missing numeric data in SAS.
    d. Calculate the subject's body mass index at each of the five visits as weight (lb) divided by height (in) squared, and then multiplied by 703.
    e. Researchers would like to study the subjects that are classified as overweight or obese at the final visit. Use PROC SQL to create a data set that limits the data to those patients with a final visit body mass index that is 25.0 or more, and to also produce a report showing the resulting data.
    f. In a comment in your program, find the 10th observation and state the subject ID, number of question variables with missing values, and the BMI at the last visit.

CHAPTER 4

Sorting, Printing, and Summarizing Your Data

Multiple Choice   **35**
Short Answer   **40**
Programming Exercises   **41**

Multiple Choice

1. Which PROC requires a BY statement?

   a. PRINT
   b. SORT
   c. FREQ
   d. All of the above

2. Which WHERE statement using a mnemonic operator is equivalent to the following WHERE statement using a symbolic operator?

   ```
   WHERE Temp ~= . ;
   ```

   a. WHERE Temp IS NOT MISSING ;
   b. WHERE Temp CONTAINS . ;
   c. WHERE Temp IN (.) ;
   d. All of the above

3. Suppose that you have a data set that includes the gender, age, and height of students in a class. Which BY statement will tell SAS to sort the data so that within each age (youngest to oldest), the data will be organized by males (tallest to shortest), followed by females (tallest to shortest)?

    a.   `BY DESCENDING Gender Age DESCENDING Height;`
    b.   `BY DESCENDING Gender DESCENDING Height Age;`
    c.   `BY Age DESCENDING Height DESCENDING Gender;`
    d.   `BY Age DESCENDING Gender DESCENDING Height;`

4. Which option in the PROC SORT statement would tell SAS to sort the following last names in alphabetical order?

    ```
    ----+----1
    de Bie
    De Leon
    deVere
    De Mesa
    Dewey
    ```

    a.   SORTSEQ = LINGUISTIC
    b.   SORTSEQ = ASCII
    c.   NODUPKEY
    d.   None of the above

5. Which of the following is a valid option for the PROC PRINT statement to suppress the Obs column from the output?

    a.   NOOBSERVATION
    b.   NOOBS
    c.   NOOBSCOL
    d.   NOOBSCOLUMN

6. To print only the variables Q1, Q2, and Q3 using PROC PRINT, which VAR statement could you use?

    a.   `VAR Q1,Q2,Q3;`
    b.   `VAR Q1 Q2 Q3;`
    c.   `VAR (Q1 to Q3);`
    d.   All of the above

7. What is true about formats assigned to variables in the DATA step?

   a. They affect the stored values of variables in the data set
   b. They need to be specified for variables during subsequent procedures where you want to use them
   c. They need to be specified for variables during subsequent DATA steps where you want to use them
   d. None of the above

8. Which of the following is a valid name for a user-defined format?

   a. Body_Mass_Index_Categories
   b. Description2
   c. Age(yrs)
   d. Varchar$

9. For the value 5678 to appear as 5,678.00 in the output which format should be used?

   a. COMMA6.2
   b. COMMA7.2
   c. COMMA7.3
   d. COMMA8.2

10. What is the purpose of using the _NULL_ keyword in a DATA statement?

    a. To create a SAS data set with zero observations
    b. To create a temporary SAS data set
    c. To delete all observations from the SAS data set
    d. To utilize the DATA step without creating a SAS data set

11. What is the purpose of using the MAXDEC = *n* option in a PROC MEANS statement?

    a. To maximize the computing power by a factor of n
    b. To limit the numeric output to n decimal places
    c. To use a maximum of n observations in the calculation
    d. None of the above

12. Which statement in PROC MEANS will produce output summarized by the values of a categorical variable?

    a. VAR
    b. OUTPUT
    c. CLASS
    d. TITLE

13. Which output-statistic-list for PROC MEANS will create two variables corresponding to the average age of females and the average age of males?

    a. MEAN(Females Males) = FemaleAge MaleAge
    b. FemaleAge MaleAge = MEAN(Females Males)
    c. MEAN(Age) = FemaleAge MaleAge
    d. FemaleAge MaleAge = MEAN(Age)

14. Which PROC uses a VALUE statement?

    a. PRINT
    b. FORMAT
    c. FREQ
    d. All of the above

15. Which PROC uses a TABLES statement?

    a. PRINT
    b. SORT
    c. FREQ
    d. All of the above

16. Which of the following procedures does not produce a report?

    a. PROC SORT
    b. PROC MEANS
    c. PROC TABULATE
    d. None of the above

17. If you wanted to produce averages and counts in the same output, what procedure could you use?

    a. PROC PRINT
    b. PROC FREQ
    c. PROC TABULATE
    d. All of the above

18. What is the order of the dimensions in a TABLE statement in PROC TABULATE?

    a. Page, row, column
    b. Page, column, row
    c. Row, column, page
    d. Column, row, page

19. If you specify just one dimension in a TABLE statement in PROC TABULATE, which dimension will you get?

    a. Rows
    b. Columns
    c. Pages
    d. You must specify at least two dimensions

20. What does PROC REPORT do by default with no additional statements or options?

    a. It will print all observations in the data set if there are any character variables
    b. It will print variables in the order that they exist in the data set
    c. It will automatically sum the data if all the variables are numeric
    d. All of the above

21. In PROC REPORT, what is the default usage type for numeric variables?

    a. ACROSS
    b. ANALYSIS
    c. DISPLAY
    d. NUMERIC

22. Which of the following is true about computed variables in PROC REPORT?

    a. They do not require a DEFINE statement
    b. They may be numeric or character
    c. They require a COMPUTE statement
    d. All of the above

Short Answer

23. Explain the differences between a title and a label when used in PROC PRINT.

24. Discuss two advantages of using a WHERE statement to subset your data rather than a subsetting IF statement.

25. Explain a situation where you would want to use an OUT= option in a PROC SORT, and another situation where you would not need to use OUT=.

26. Suppose that you have a data set that contains a subject ID, name, address, city, state, and ZIP code. You would like to de-identify the results of a PROC PRINT so that only the subject ID and ZIP code appear in the output. Would you use a WHERE statement or a VAR statement? Explain your choice.

27. Explain the difference between a format and an informat.

28. Explain the difference between a function and a format.

29. Suppose you have a variable called Gender that stores a value of 1 for males and a 2 for females. Discuss why creating a user-defined format to print a 1 as 'Male' and a 2 as 'Female' may be better than creating a new character variable in a DATA step and then printing the character variable.

30. Discuss two advantages of using the keyword _NULL_ in the DATA statement when writing data to a text file.

31. Describe an advantage of using the CLASS statement rather than the BY statement with PROC MEANS.

32. Explain the difference between using a MEAN function in a DATA step to calculate an average versus using PROC MEANS to calculate an average.

33. Suppose that you need to present simple descriptive statistics to the Principal Investigator of the study that you work on. Would it be necessary to use an OUTPUT statement when using PROC MEANS to generate these simple descriptive statistics?

34. Name two other procedures that can produce some of the same results as PROC TABULATE. Explain your choices.

35. Describe two differences between PROC REPORT and PROC TABULATE.

36. Creating a report with PROC TABULATE or PROC REPORT can be more time-consuming than with PROC MEANS and PROC FREQ. Describe why you might want to make this time investment.

Programming Exercises

37. The SAS data set named CRAYONS contains information on standard Crayola crayon colors. The variables in this file are crayon number, color name, hexadecimal code, RGB triplet, pack added, year issued, and year retired.

   a. In a comment in your code, describe how you could view the variable attributes in this SAS data set.
   b. Using the method described in part a), review the names, labels, and attributes of the variables in the SAS data set CRAYONS. Record the label and length for the variable Color as a comment in your program.
   c. Calculate the number of colors issued per year. Add a comment to your code stating in which year the largest number of colors were issued.
   d. Sorting the crayons by color using their names would be ineffective due to the uniqueness of the names, but the information found in the RGB triplets can be used instead. Sort the crayon data by RGB triplet.
   e. Print the sorted data showing only columns for the variables color name and RGB triplet.

38. The Coastal Humane Society is preparing their year-end donation receipts for each person who contributed money during the year. The raw data file Donations.dat contains variables to identify the donor ID, first and last name, and their address information as well as individual records for each amount and month donated.

   a. After examining the raw data file, read the file Donations.dat into SAS.
   b. Create a text file containing one report for each donor using the following example for variables, formats, text, and layout.

```
TO: James Cunningham
    12390 Poplar Dr.
    McKinleyville, CA 95519

Thank you for your support! Your donations
help us to save hundreds of cats and dogs
each year.

Donations to Coastal Humane Society
(Tax ID: 99-5551212)
Apr  $95.00
Apr  $110.00
May  $55.00
```

   c. Include code that places a page break between each donor receipt.

39. The United States Bureau of Labor Statistics publishes various indexes that measure average prices of consumer goods in urban areas. The SAS data set called GAS contains data on the average price of unleaded regular gasoline (per gallon) for recent years by month in the United States. The variables in this file are year, month, and average gasoline price.

    a.   Review the names, labels, and attributes of the variables in the SAS data set GAS. Record the label and variable type for GasPrice as a comment in your program.
    b.   Identify the minimum and maximum gasoline price per year. Present the price statistics to two decimal places.
    c.   Create a new variable that represents the quarter of the year by applying a user-defined format to the Month variable in a DATA step.
    d.   Using the data from part c) calculate the average and standard deviation of gasoline prices per quarter per year. Present the price statistics to two decimal places.
    e.   Create a SAS data set that contains the averages and standard deviations as calculated in part d). Print the data set showing only the year, quarter, average price, and standard deviation. Present the price statistics with a dollar sign and two decimal places.

40. The World Health Organization (WHO) collected data in countries across the world regarding the outbreak of swine flu cases and deaths in 2009. The data in the SAS data set called SFF includes information on cases and deaths per country by month during the epidemic.

    a.   Review the names, labels, and attributes of the variables in the SAS data set SFF. Record the name and length of the character variables as a comment in your program.
    b.   Count the number of countries within each continent.
    c.   Count the number of countries per continent that reported no cases during the first month of the outbreak (April) versus the number of countries per continent that had at least one case. Do the same for the last month of the outbreak (August).
    d.   To find potential errors in the data, create a report for countries that reported a first death date, but reported no first case date. This output should include only the variables continent, country, first case date, last reported number of cases, and first death date.
    e.   Add code that will organize the report from part d) so that the countries on the same continent are grouped together, and make sure that dates are presentable.

41. A gourmet pizza restaurant is considering adding new toppings to its menu. Each month they survey ten customers to rate their preferences for three different toppings. The SAS data set called PIZZARATINGS contains data for respondent ID, topping type, and rating.

    a.   Review the names, labels, and attributes of the variables in the SAS data set PIZZARATINGS. Record the label and variable type for Rating as a comment in your program.
    b.   Create a format to be used on the Rating variable so that the data values are presented as n/a (missing values), never (1), might (2), at least once (3), occasionally (4), and often (5). Apply this format to a listing of the data set.

    c.   For each topping type, count the number of nonmissing observations and calculate the average rating. Present the count as a whole number and the average to three decimal places.

    d.   Repeat part c) using a different procedure.

42. A regional SAS conference will be held in a few weeks' time. The SAS data set called CONFERENCE contains information about the registered attendees and their participation at the event.

    a.   Examine this SAS data set including the variable labels and attributes. Count the number of attendees for each registration type.

    b.   Create a format that will present the VegMeal variable (which indicates whether the attendee requires a vegetarian meal) as Yes or No, and apply this format to a listing of the data set.

    c.   Create one table that shows the total registration paid per area code, as well as the total paid by registration type within area code. Be sure to present the totals using a dollar sign and two decimal places.

    d.   Create one table that presents the number of attendees and overall percentage per area code and registration type, as well as a total count and percentage for each area code. Do not include statistics in this table other than those requested. Be sure to present the number of attendees without decimal places, and the overall percentage to two decimal places.

    e.   Repeat part d) using a different procedure.

43. A California-based exercise equipment company makes six different models of elliptical trainers. The company's management is interested in reviewing shipping records and sales over the last month, and would like your assistance. The SAS data set called ELLIPTICAL contains individual purchases and has variables for machine type, machine cost, shipped to state, shipped to ZIP code, sales tax, and shipping cost.

    a.   Examine this SAS data set including the variable labels and attributes. Calculate the average shipping cost per state, excluding the state of California.

    b.   Using a procedure, calculate the total cost including tax and shipping, and present this total cost for each individual purchase organized by state and machine.

    c.   Use your code from part b) to calculate the total cost for heart rate monitor (HRT) machines only. Present the grand total cost for all HRT machine purchases organized by region (defined as West Coast = California, Oregon, and Washington versus all others). Also include a breakdown, by type of HRT machine, of the total number of purchases within each region.

44. The official results of the 2012 London Olympics men's 3-meter springboard diving finals can be found in the SAS data set called DIVING. The 2012 Olympic games were the first to use a new overall scoring method for diving. The data consist of six observations per diver, one for each of their six dives in the final event. The variables in this file are diver's name, country, height (m), weight (kg), dive number (1 to 6), dive code, degree of difficulty, description, position, scores from each of seven judges, penalty, old scoring method, and new scoring method. Use *only procedures* to complete the following tasks.

a. Examine this SAS data set including the variable labels and attributes. Compute the overall mean, minimum, and maximum of the two scoring methods.

b. Calculate the total score per diver by summing the new scoring method scores for all dives. Output this information to a data set, sort, and then print it to determine which divers received the gold (highest total score), silver, and bronze medals for this event. Include a comment in your code stating the name of each medalist.

c. Count the numeric scores given to each diver by each judge according to the following judging criteria groupings: <0.5 = Completely Failed, 0.5 to <2.5 = Unsatisfactory, 2.5 to <5 = Deficient, 5 to <7 = Satisfactory, 7 to <8.5 = Good, 8.5 to <9.5 = Very Good, and 9.5+ = Excellent.

d. Calculate the minimum and maximum score per dive for each diver. Be sure to present your results by diver and in dive number order.

CHAPTER 5

Enhancing Your Output with ODS

Multiple Choice

1. Which procedure allows you to view a list of all the names of the built-in SAS styles for output?

    a.   PRINT
    b.   TEMPLATE
    c.   REPORT
    d.   TABULATE

2. Which ODS destination is a default for procedure output?

    a.   HTML
    b.   OUTPUT
    c.   PDF
    d.   RTF

3. The Output Delivery System does which of the following?

    a.   It determines what the output will look like
    b.   It cannot be turned off
    c.   It does not belong to a DATA step or PROC step
    d.   All of the above

4.   To exclude procedure names from output, you use which statement?

   a.   ODS NOPROCNAME
   b.   ODS TITLEEXCLUDE
   c.   ODS NOPROCTITLE
   d.   None of the above

5.   When creating HTML output, which of the following options, along with the PATH option, will create a file that contains the results?

   a.   FILE=
   b.   BODY=
   c.   Both can be used
   d.   Neither can be used

6.   Which of the following is true about the ODS LISTING destination?

   a.   It creates high-resolution reports and graphics
   b.   It does not use a style for tabular output
   c.   It cannot send output to a file
   d.   All of the above

7.   Which TITLE statement option requires hexadecimal coding?

   a.   COLOR=
   b.   BCOLOR=
   c.   FONT=
   d.   None of the above

8.   By default, SAS titles use what font attribute?

   a.   BOLD
   b.   ITALIC
   c.   Both of the above
   d.   Neither of the above

9.   Using the STYLE= option in PROC PRINT will have no impact on which of the following types of ODS output?

   a.   LISTING
   b.   HTML
   c.   RTF
   d.   PDF

10. To apply a STYLE= option to some, but not all, of the variables in a PROC PRINT, which of the following could you do?

    a. Specify the STYLE= option in the PROC PRINT statement
    b. Use more than one VAR statement
    c. Use a SUM statement
    d. Use an ID statement

11. To apply a STYLE= option to some, but not all of the variables in a PROC REPORT, which of the following could you do?

    a. Specify the STYLE= option in the PROC REPORT statement
    b. Use more than one COLUMN statement
    c. Specify the STYLE= option in a DEFINE statement for each individual variable
    d. Specify the STYLE= option in a BREAK statement

12. To change the appearance of a data cell, which of the following PROC TABULATE statements would you use?

    a. CLASS
    b. CLASSLEV
    c. TABLE
    d. VAR

13. Which of the following procedures must always be used to create reports with trafficlighting?

    a. FORMAT
    b. PRINT
    c. REPORT
    d. TABULATE

14. Which style attribute could you use to modify the appearance of text in a data cell?

    a. FONTFAMILY
    b. TEXTALIGN
    c. COLOR
    d. All of the above

15. A data set can be created using which of the following ODS statements?

    a. TRACE
    b. SELECT
    c. EXCLUDE
     d. OUTPUT

16. Which ODS statement does not require you to specify an output object?

    a. TRACE
    b. SELECT
    c. EXCLUDE
    d. OUTPUT

Short Answer

17. Explain the main difference between the STYLE= option in an ODS statement and the STYLE= option in PROC PRINT?

18. Describe the appearance of the title created by the following TITLE statement.

```
TITLE FONT = Arial 'For Average Sales '
      COLOR = BLUE BOLD
      'Click Here. '
      JUSTIFY = RIGHT HEIGHT = 16PT COLOR = BLACK
      'Thanks!';
```

19. Explain the difference between using a STYLE= option in the PROC TABULATE statement versus using a STYLE= option in the TABLE statement.

20. Suppose the following user-defined format is created to be used in a PROC PRINT. What will be the result if the format is applied to a numeric variable in a FORMAT statement? What will be the result if the format is applied to the cell COLOR or FOREGROUND attribute in a STYLE= option?

```
PROC FORMAT;
   VALUE rng 0 -< 50 = 'red'
            50 -< 70 = 'yellow'
            70 - HIGH = 'green';
RUN;
```

21. What is the main difference between setting a style attribute equal to a user-defined format versus setting a style attribute equal to a specific value?

22. Describe why you might choose to use ODS SELECT over ODS EXCLUDE or vice versa.

23. Explain why it is important to be careful about where you put ODS statements in your program.

Programming Exercises

24. The United States Geological Survey provides data on earthquakes of historical interest. The SAS data set called EARTHQUAKES contains data about earthquakes with a magnitude greater than 2.5 in the United States and its territories. The variables are year, month, day, state, and magnitude.

    a. Examine this SAS data set including the variable labels and attributes. Count the number of earthquakes that were classified as Major to Great events (magnitude 7.0 or more) for each state.
    b. Add an ODS statement to your program in part a) that will capture these counts in a SAS data set.
    c. Using these counts, create a PDF report listing the states with at least two Major to Great events. Modify the report by eliminating the procedure title, using the ANALYSIS style, including only the variables for state and the count, and adding a meaningful title.
    d. On the same page as the results for part c), list the earthquakes classified as Major to Great events since the year 2000.

25. The SAS data set named CRAYONS contains information on standard Crayola crayon colors. The variables in this file are crayon number, color name, hexadecimal code, RGB triplet, pack size, year issued, and year retired.

    a. Examine this SAS data set including the variable labels and attributes. Create a table showing counts by year of issue. Also create a report listing the color name, hexadecimal code, and year of issue for each crayon. Send these two reports to the default output destination.
    b. Add code that will save the output in a text file.
    c. Add code that will save the output in an HTML file.
    d. Add code that will save the output in an RTF file.
    e. Add code that will save the output in a PDF file.

26. A local company has decided to try advertising for an open position of Administrative Assistant at their company on a jobs website. After the filing deadline passed, they received a file back with the information from over 1,000 applicants. The SAS data set called APPLICATIONS contains data from all of the applicants. The variables are the name, typing speed, desired pay, qualification check boxes (a comma separated variable containing combinations of codes 1 through 6), and start date.

   a. Examine this SAS data set including the variable labels and attributes. Create a report that will allow the management to see counts of the typing speed, qualification check boxes, and desired pay.

   b. Limit the report from part a) to applicants who can start by the end of April, know Microsoft Word, can work full-time, and live locally. Include a main title with a larger font to indicate that this table is a subset of the applicant pool. Subtitles should list the criteria used in selecting applicants.

   c. Now that the management is happier with the size of the applicant pool, they would like a listing of the name, start date, and desired pay. Organize the list by typing speed (<40 wpm = Slow, 40-<80 wpm = Medium, and 80 or more = Fast). Include a main title with a larger font to indicate that this listing is for internal review. Subtitles should list the criteria used in selecting applicants.

   d. To facilitate review, management would like the results of part c) presented in two report formats. The first format should be an HTML file that can be posted on an internal website. The second format should be a file that can be opened in Microsoft Word and printed for managers that prefer a hard copy.

   e. For the two reports from part d), format the cells for name and starting date with a gray background, and the cells for desired pay a green background with white and bold font.

27. Suppose that you have mortgage application data from a national bank with five branches in California contained in the SAS data set called LOANAPP. The Board of Directors would like an executive summary to assess their fixed-rate, home loan applicants with a comparison of the five branches. They are particularly concerned about loans that have less than 5% on the down payment. Variables in this data set include the identification information for the applicant, credit score, loan information, home price, and the down payment as a percentage of the sales price.

   a. Examine this SAS data set including the variable labels and attributes. Create a table that provides information about the number and percent of loan approvals within each branch for loans with less than 5% down. Be sure to format and label variables so that they are presentation-ready in the output.

   b. Create a table that calculates the count, mean loan amount, mean home price, and median credit score, by branch for all approved loans. Format the loan and price data to include dollar signs, commas, and decimal places, and format the count and credit score to be whole numbers. Center justify all values in the data cells of the table.

    c. For your tables in parts a) and b) create a main title with a larger font to explain the contents of the table and a second title with a slightly smaller font to explain the subsetting of the data.

    d. Send the output to an ODS destination that creates output that managers can open in Microsoft Word. The tables should appear in separate columns on the same page.

28. A study was conducted to see whether taking vitamin E daily would reduce the levels of atherosclerotic disease in a random sample of 500 individuals. Clinical measurements, including thickness of plaque of the carotid artery (taken via ultrasound), were recorded at baseline and a final visit. Researchers evaluated the change (before minus after) in plaque thickness by treatment group and strata with a series of four paired *t* tests. The results were output using ODS OUTPUT to a SAS data set called PVALUES that requires formatting in order to produce a presentation-ready report.

    a. Examine this SAS data set including the variable labels and attributes. Using the information found in the variable labels, format the values for strata and treatment to indicate which strata and treatment group are being compared and create a listing of the data. Format the mean and confidence limits to three decimal places.

    b. Modify the labels for the strata and treatment variables to be more concise. Include these labels on the output.

    c. The variables on the resulting output should be presented in this order: treatment, strata, mean difference, lower and upper confidence interval for the mean, and p-value. All columns should be centered.

    d. Bold and italicize p-values that show a significant difference at the 0.05 level in mean plaque thickness before and after treatment.

    e. Send the output to a file that researchers can open in Adobe Acrobat.

29. An instructor at the local university teaches three sections of the same statistics course during a term. The SAS data set called GRADES has one observation per student. The variables are the course-section number, individual scores for each of the three exams, and a student ID.

    a. Examine this SAS data set including the variable labels and attributes. The instructor would like to list the data for course-section, ID, and exam scores organized by lowest to highest score for the third exam within each section of the course. Include centered titles that reflect the type of data in the main title (at 14-point bolded font) and the sort order in a subtitle (with Arial font and no bolding).

    b. Use a procedure to create another listing of the data for course-section, ID, and an average of the three exams for each student. If this average is below 0.60, the cell should be colored red. If it is between 0.60 and <0.80, the cell should be colored yellow. If it is 0.80 or higher, the cell should be colored green.

    c. Add programming to the listing from part b) to also display the variables for the individual exam scores and repeat the coloring scheme, but this time apply it to the cell text with the cell background color being light gray.

d. Use a procedure to create another table that calculates the course-section average for each exam formatted to three decimal places. If the average score for the exam was 0.80 or better, highlight this cell in pink.

CHAPTER 6

Modifying and Combining SAS Data Sets

Multiple Choice

1. The data sets APR, MAY, and JUN have one observation for each day in the corresponding month. How many observations will be in the resulting data set called MONTHS?

    ```
    DATA months;
      SET apr may jun;
    RUN;
    ```

    a. 0
    b. 30
    c. 60
    d. 91

2. Which statement is required when interleaving data sets but not when stacking data sets?

    a. SET
    b. BY
    c. MERGE
    d. UPDATE

3. Suppose the SAS data sets called ONE and TWO contain the following data. How many observations will be in the resulting SAS data set called FIRST?

    ONE

ID	Date
123	12/31/2013
456	09/15/2014

    TWO

ID	Date
123	05/04/2014
123	06/22/2014
333	01/09/2014
456	11/16/2013

    ```
    DATA first;
      SET one two;
       BY ID;
    RUN;
    ```

    a. 0
    b. 2
    c. 4
    d. 6

4. Using the preceding SAS data sets called ONE and TWO and the following DATA step, how many observations will be in the resulting SAS data set called SECOND?

    ```
    DATA second;
      MERGE one two;
       BY ID;
    RUN;
    ```

    a. 0
    b. 2
    c. 4
    d. 6

5. Suppose you would like to use the following program to combine the SAS data set DEMOGRAPHICS, which contains the variables ID, Age, Gender, and Date, with the SAS data set MEDICALHX, which contains the variables ID, PreviousTreatment, and Date. Assume that both data sets are sorted by ID. Which of the following will happen?

   ```
   DATA patients;
     MERGE demographics medicalhx;
       BY ID;
   RUN;
   ```

   a. The variable Date in DEMOGRAPHICS will overwrite the variable Date in MEDICALHX for observations with common ID values
   b. The variable Date in MEDICALHX will overwrite the variable Date in DEMOGRAPHICS for observations with common ID values
   c. Both Date variables will be included as separate variables
   d. SAS will give you an error message

6. What happens if you try to combine data sets using a MERGE statement in a DATA step, but you do not include a BY statement?

   a. You will get an ERROR message and your program will not run
   b. You will get a WARNING message and your program will not run
   c. A NOTE will appear in the log telling you that the data are not properly sorted
   d. None of the above

7. Suppose you are given a SAS data set that contains the GPAs of students in a certain college with seven majors of study. You want to create a variable that is the difference between the GPA of each individual student and the mean GPA of all students with the same major. One method for doing this requires that you first create a data set that has the mean GPA for each of the seven majors. What steps would you take to calculate the mean GPA?

   a. Use PROC MEANS with an OUTPUT and a BY statement
   b. Use PROC MEANS with an OUTPUT and a CLASS statement
   c. Use the MEAN function in a DATA step
   d. Either A or B will work

8. Suppose you are given one SAS data set that contains the GPAs of students in a certain college with seven majors of study and a second SAS data set with just one observation containing a variable for the overall average GPA in the college (CollegeGPA). How can you combine the two data sets so that the value for the variable CollegeGPA will be repeated for all observations in the data set of students?

    a.   In a DATA step using a MERGE and a BY statement
    b.   In a DATA step using a MERGE without a BY statement
    c.   In a DATA step using two SET statements
    d.   In a DATA step using one SET statement and a BY statement

9. Which SQL clause identifies the matching variables to be used for an inner join?

    a.   SELECT
    b.   FROM
    c.   WHERE
    d.   GROUPBY

10. Consider the following SAS data set and program. What value will be calculated for AvgExam1 for the third observation?

    EXAMS

SID	Group	Exam1	Exam2	Exam3
092363	Major	80	75	85
057781	Major	65	85	75
082944	Minor	85	90	90
089813	Minor	70	70	80

    ```
    PROC SQL;
      CREATE TABLE e1avg AS
      SELECT *, MEAN(Exam1) AS AvgExam1
      FROM exams;
    RUN;
    ```

    a.   .
    b.   72.5
    c.   75
    d.   77.5

11. Updating a master data set with transactions is most similar to which data-combining method?

    a.   Stacking
    b.   Interleaving
    c.   Merging
    d.   Tracking

12. Consider the following SAS data set and program. How many variables will be in the resulting data set called PAYTYPE?

    EMPLOYEES

ID	Gender	Age	Hours	Wage
1234	Male	32	25	25.20
4567	Female	28	40	17.80
8910	Male	25	40	19.45
3456	Female	20	22	10.50

    ```
    DATA paytype (DROP = Hours Wage);
      SET employees (DROP = Age);
      Pay = Hours * Wage;
    RUN;
    ```

    a. 1
    b. 3
    c. 4
    d. 5

13. Consider the preceding EMPLOYEES data set. Suppose the following program was written to select one observation per gender. What needs to be added for this program to carry out this task correctly?

    ```
    DATA paygender (DROP = Hours Wage);
      SET employees (DROP = Age);
      BY Gender;
      IF FIRST.Gender = 1;
    RUN;
    ```

    a. Rank = _N_;
    b. IF _ERROR_ = 0;
    c. PROC SORT DATA = employees; BY Gender; RUN;
    d. None of the above

14. Which data set option allows you to track during a merge whether a given data set contributed data to the current observation?

    a. KEEP=
    b. OBS=
    c. IN=
    d. WHERE=

15. What data set option will not impact which observations will be read into a SAS data set?

    a. DROP=
    b. FIRSTOBS=
    c. OBS=
    d. WHERE=

16. Which statement in PROC TRANSPOSE specifies the variables that will not be transposed in the resulting data set?

    a. PROC TRANSPOSE
    b. BY
    c. ID
    d. VAR

17. Suppose you read the following raw data with the accompanying INPUT statement. What will be the value of the automatic variable _N_ for the last observation in the data set?

    ```
    ----+----1--
    123    27
    456    XX
    789    32
    012    31
    345    XX

    INPUT ID Age;
    ```

    a. 0
    b. 1
    c. 2
    d. 5

18. Given the preceding raw data and INPUT statement, what will be the value of the automatic variable _ERROR_ for the last observation in the data set?

    a. 0
    b. 1
    c. 2
    d. 5

Short Answer

19. Describe a situation where you might want to stack two SAS data sets rather than interleave them.

20. Suppose an instructor has two SAS data sets with student grades, one for each of the sections that he is teaching this term. Both data sets contain the variables StudentName, StudentID, and FinalScore. He would like to combine these data sets so that he can use one PROC MEANS to calculate descriptive statistics to be compared between the sections. Describe one way to combine the data and what statements would be required in PROC MEANS.

21. What would you do if you found the following message in your SAS log when performing a one-to-many merge?

```
NOTE: MERGE statement has more than one data set
      with repeats of BY values.
```

22. Discuss which would be more effective: using a procedure to calculate a descriptive statistic of interest and then merging it back into the original data set for comparison, or viewing the results of the procedure and then typing the value of the statistic into a DATA step.

23. Describe any advantages of using PROC SQL to join SAS data sets or to add summary statistics compared to the traditional SAS programming methods that use a MERGE statement in a DATA step.

24. Suppose that you have a SAS data set with 20 observations and one variable called ID. You would like to repeat each observation five times, making a total of 100 observations. Would it be better to do this using a DATA step with an OUTPUT statement in an iterative DO group or using PROC TRANSPOSE?

25. Describe the difference between using a WHERE= option in the DATA statement versus in a SET statement.

26. Suppose the following SAS data set called PARTICIPANTS is read in a DATA step using a SET statement as well as BY Gender Height. Explain the difference between FIRST.Gender and FIRST.Height, and indicate which observations will have a value of 1 for these automatic variables.

PARTICIPANTS

Name	Gender	Height
JoAnn	F	64
Jane	F	66
Joyce	F	68
David	M	69
Stan	M	70
Jim	M	71
Bob	M	71

Programming Exercises

27. The BabyCentre website publishes the top 10 baby names by gender in various countries. The names of girls and boys are listed in order of ranking (where observation one is the most popular name and observation 10 is the 10th most popular name) in SAS data sets called AUSTRALIA, BRAZIL, FRANCE, INDIA, RUSSIA, and UNITEDSTATES.

    a. Examine these SAS data sets including the variable labels and attributes. Create a new variable in each data set that is equal to the popularity rank for each name.
    b. Combine the data sets by stacking, and sort the resulting data set by popularity ranking. Make sure that the resulting data set has only one variable for boys names and one variable for girls names.
    c. Alternatively, combine the data sets using interleaving by ranking.
    d. Add programming to the DATA step created in part c) to create a variable that represents the name of the country.
    e. Add a comment to your program that states the number of observations and variables in the final data set from part d).

28. The local school district has a SAS data set called DISTRICT that contains the rubric used for classifying teachers' annual evaluations. The rubric is based on two components: a teacher score and a curriculum grade. Using these components, an overall rating for the teacher can be determined. The data for 10 elementary school teachers who are due for evaluation are stored in the SAS data set called TEACHERS.

    a. Examine these SAS data sets including the variable labels and attributes. Combine the two SAS data sets with a DATA step so that the district rating is properly assigned to each teacher.
    b. In the same DATA step as part a), eliminate any observation that does not match to a teacher.

c. Sort the resulting data set by teacher name so that administrators can easily locate each teacher's rating.
d. Repeat parts a) and b) using PROC SQL.
e. Add a comment to your program that states the number of observations and variables in the final data set from part c).

29. The United States Bureau of Labor Statistics publishes various indexes that measure average prices of consumer goods in urban areas. The SAS data set AVEPRICES contains data on the average price of unleaded regular gasoline (per gallon), whole large eggs (per dozen), and whole milk (per gallon) for a 14-year period by month in the United States. The variables in this file are year, month, price, and type of commodity.

a. Examine this SAS data set including the variable labels and attributes. Use one or more procedures to create a data set that contains the average price per year for each commodity.
b. Using one or more procedures, create a new version of this data set that has 12 variables corresponding to each month, that contain the price data for each combination of commodity and year.
c. Combine the averages calculated in part a) with the data set created in part b).
d. In one DATA step, divide the data set from part c) into three data sets that correspond to the three commodities.
e. Add code to the DATA step in part d) that will give the variables for months better names. The final data sets should not include any automatic variables that may have been created along the way.
f. Add a comment to your program that states the number of observations and variables in each of the final data sets created in part e).

30. Researchers at a local medical center have just completed enrollment for a clinical trial of a new cholesterol-lowering medication for use in subjects with borderline high total cholesterol. They keep their enrollment data in two SAS data sets so as to not bias the clinicians. The VISITS data set contains basic information about each subject at their baseline visit (Visit = 0). The TXGROUP data set contains information about whether the subject received the treatment or a placebo.

a. Examine these SAS data sets including the variable labels and attributes. Combine these two data sources to create a data set that identifies the treatment group for each subject.
b. The data entry clerk informs you that there may be duplicate records in the TXGROUP data set. Write code that will identify any duplicate entries and modify the programming for part a), if necessary.
c. Using the combined data set from part b), calculate the median baseline cholesterol measurement across all subjects, and use this information to create a variable that groups subjects as less than or equal to the median, or more than the median. Do this without typing the calculated median value by hand into your code.

d. Using the data set from part c), create another data set that schedules subjects for their next three visits, one every 30 days starting at the baseline visit date, for a total of four visits per subject. Each of the visits should appear as a new observation with the original subject information, the median grouping, the corresponding visit date, and a visit number (0, 1, 2, or 3).

e. Add a comment to your program that states the number of observations and variables in the final data sets created in parts c) and d).

31. Information Technology Services (ITS) at Central State University has a computing service called "the Grid," which is offered to faculty, staff, and students. ITS tracks information on registered users in a SAS data set called USERS and information about the projects that they have registered on the Grid in a SAS data set called PROJECTS. Users are allowed to register more than one project at a time. However, only one project can actually be processed at a time.

a. Examine these SAS data sets including the variable labels and attributes. Add a comment to your program that notes the sort order of the variables in these data sets.

b. Combine the USERS and PROJECTS data sets into one SAS data set using a DATA step.

c. In the same DATA step as part b), create three SAS data sets for incomplete projects (no end date), completed projects (with an end date), and users with no registered projects.

d. In the same DATA step as part c), create a variable that is a cumulative count of the number of projects completed by each user for the completed projects data set only.

e. Recreate the completed projects data set using PROC SQL. This time instead of a cumulative counter variable calculate the total number of completed projects per user.

f. Add a comment to your program that states the number of observations and variables in each of the final data sets created in part d).

32. The SAS data set called ILUVTHE80S contains data on the top 100 songs of the Eighties as ranked by the cable television network VH1. The variables in the data set include information such as the band, title, genre, and length of the song.

a. Examine this SAS data set including the variable labels and attributes. Create a variable that counts the total number of songs per band.

b. Calculate the median length of songs for each genre.

c. Using a DATA step, combine the median length from part b) with the original data and counter variable from part a) into one final data set. This final data set should be sorted by band name, and should not include any automatic variables that may have been created along the way.

d. Repeat parts a), b), and c) using PROC SQL.

e. Examine the results from parts a), b), and c), and state in a comment in your program the number of bands, and number of genres in the data set. Also, state the total number of observations in the original and final data sets.

33. The local school district wants to survey all sixth grade students and their school-aged siblings. There are three different types of surveys: one for the sixth graders, one for their younger siblings, and one for their older siblings. The SAS data set called SCHOOLSURVEY contains data for all sixth graders in the three middle schools in the district (Rachael Carson, Green Valley, and Redwood Grove). The data set also includes data for all their siblings attending schools in the district, which can be linked back to the sixth grader by Family_ID.

    a. Examine this SAS data set including the variable labels and attributes. Add a comment to your program that notes the sort order of the variables in this data set.
    b. Create a data set that has one observation for each sixth grader.
    c. Combine the data set from part b) with the original data, and create a variable that is the age difference in years between the sixth grader and the sibling.
    d. Count the number of older siblings and the number of younger siblings of the sixth grader, and add these variables to the data set of just the sixth graders. Be sure to label the variables appropriately.
    e. So the district knows how many surveys to print and distribute to each school, compute the number of sixth graders, and the total number of younger and older siblings by school. Be sure to show the complete names for the schools.
    f. For each sixth grader, add variables to your data set for the age difference between the sixth grader and their youngest sibling, and the age difference between the sixth grader and their oldest sibling.
    g. For each school, compute the average, minimum, and maximum age difference between the sixth graders and their youngest and oldest siblings. Be sure to show the complete names for the schools.

34. A wildlife rescue center maintains a database consisting of two SAS data sets called FRIENDS and NEWINFO. The FRIENDS data set contains one observation for each supporter. Every time the center receives a donation, the staff add an observation to the NEWINFO data set. They also add an observation to NEWINFO every time there is a new volunteer or a change of address. To create an up-to-date data set of supporters, the staff need to combine the NEWINFO data set with the FRIENDS data set.

    a. Examine these SAS data sets including the variable labels and attributes. Add a comment to your program that notes the sort order of the observations in these data sets. Then state the number of variables that appear in both data sets, and the number of variables that appear in just the FRIENDS data set or just the NEWINFO data set.
    b. Add the information in the NEWINFO data set to the FRIENDS data set. Do not add any new variables to the FRIENDS data set. Be sure to make a backup copy of the FRIENDS data set before modifying it.
    c. The staff would like to see a report showing the total donations received from each friend. Compute the total donations by ID, and combine the totals with the FRIENDS data. Then produce a report listing the ID, first and last name, and total donations for each friend.

CHAPTER 7

Writing Flexible Code with the SAS Macro Facility

Multiple Choice

1. Which of the following is a valid macro variable name?

    a. 01_01_1960
    b. _SP4EVR_
    c. Charlie'sPlace
    d. S.O.S.

2. If the following code is submitted and then followed by a PROC PRINT, what will be the resulting title in the output?

    ```
    %LET title = The Amazing Race;
    TITLE '&title';
    ```

    a. The Amazing Race
    b. &title
    c. title
    d. '&title'

3. If the following code is submitted and then followed by a PROC PRINT, what will be the resulting title in the output?

    ```
    %LET title = The Amazing Race;
    TITLE "&title";
    ```

    a. The Amazing Race
    b. &title
    c. title
    d. '&title'

4. If the following code is submitted and then followed by a PROC PRINT, what will be the resulting title in the output?

    ```
    %LET title = The Amazing Race;
    TITLE 'title';
    ```

    a. The Amazing Race
    b. &title
    c. title
    d. '&title'

5. Suppose that the following code is submitted to assign a libref name to a macro variable called &lib. Which PROC PRINT will create output for the SAS data set called SASHELP.CARS?

    ```
    %LET lib = sashelp;
    ```

    a. PROC PRINT DATA = &lib.cars; RUN;
    b. PROC PRINT DATA = &lib..cars; RUN;
    c. PROC PRINT DATA = "&lib.cars"; RUN;
    d. PROC PRINT DATA = "&lib..cars"; RUN;

6. Which macro call will invoke the macro named %GETIT?

    a. %GETIT
    b. %GETIT;
    c. %GETIT();
    d. All of the above

7. Which of the following refers to a local macro variable?

    a. `TITLE "Report run on &SYSDATE";`
    b. `%LET report = new;`
    c. ```
        %MACRO lst(dsn=);
            PROC CONTENTS DATA = &dsn;
            RUN;
        %MEND lst;
        ```
    d.  All of the above

8.  What is true about conditional macro logic statements such as %IF-%THEN?

    a.  They appear in the program after macro resolution
    b.  They can be used to apply logic to sections of code
    c.  They are only used to create variables in a data set
    d.  None of the above

9.  Which CALL SYMPUTX statement correctly assigns a value to a macro variable called &dflag based on the SAS data set variable called X?

    a.  `CALL SYMPUTX("dflag",X);`
    b.  `CALL SYMPUTX(dflag,"X");`
    c.  `CALL SYMPUTX("dflag","X");`
    d.  `CALL SYMPUTX(dflag,X);`

10. Which of the following will automatically create a macro variable that can be used later on in the same macro?

    a.  %IF-%THEN/%ELSE statements
    b.  %IF-%THEN-%DO-%END statements
    c.  %DO loops
    d.  All of the above

11. Which SQL clause is required to produce a macro variable?

    a.  INTO
    b.  HAVING
    c.  Both are required
    d.  Neither is required
        ```

12. Which system option will not show the value of a macro variable after resolution?

    a. MERROR
    b. MLOGIC
    c. MPRINT
    d. SYMBOLGEN

Short Answer

13. Describe how using macro variables in your programming can make your code more flexible.

14. Why is it a good idea to write standard SAS code first before adding macro logic?

15. Explain why double quotation marks are important for the following TITLE statement.

    ```
    TITLE "Passage Rate on &SYSDAY";
    ```

16. Explain why the macro variable &n does not require double quotation marks in the following DATA step.

    ```
    %LET n = 12;

    DATA ampm;
       SET times;
       NewTime = OldTime + &n;
    RUN;
    ```

17. What is the difference between a macro variable and a macro?

18. Suppose you have a long SAS program that includes many DATA steps and procedures. The logic of the program depends on the date on which the data were downloaded, which is referenced throughout the program. Describe a way that you could use macro concepts to save time and prevent mistakes when the date changes.

19. What is a parameter in a macro, and why would you want to use one?

20. Determine whether it would be better to use the TODAY() function or the &SYSDATE macro variable to calculate age as of today based on a date of birth. Then explain why.

Programming Exercises

21. The SAS data set called CATS contains information about breeds of cats. The variables are the name of the breed, the place where the breed originated, how the breed was derived, the type of hair, and a description of the breed's appearance. The following program produces counts of breed by place of origin, and then prints a report listing all the data for breeds that originated in Thailand. Modify the program using macro variables and a macro to increase its flexibility.

```
LIBNAME sasdata 'c:\MySASLib';

** Original code without macro variables;
PROC FREQ DATA = sasdata.cats;
   TABLES Origin;
   TITLE 'Cat Breeds by Origin';
RUN;

PROC PRINT DATA = sasdata.cats;
   WHERE Origin = 'Thailand';
   TITLE 'Cat Breeds with Origin = Thailand';
RUN;
```

   a. Examine this SAS data set including the variable labels and attributes. Use %LET statements to create two macro variables: one to replace the variable name Origin, and another to replace the data value 'Thailand'. Use an option that will enable you to see the standard SAS statements generated by the macro processor.
   b. Use the macro variables to produce counts for the variable Derivation, and to list data for breeds that were derived by mutation.
   c. Convert the code to a macro. Pass the values for the two macro variables into the macro as parameters. Call the macro to produce counts for the variable Hair, and to list data for breeds with long hair.
   d. Add programming to your macro from part c) that will save your output in a PDF file. Name this file CatRpt, and append the filename with a suffix that is the name of the variable used in the TABLES statement.

22. The National Oceanic and Atmospheric Administration (NOAA) tracks oceanographic data at stations across the United States. The SAS data set called VIRGINIAKEY contains meteorological data for one year for the Virginia Key station located near Miami, Florida.

   a. Examine this SAS data set including the variable labels and attributes. Create a frequency report for month and another report that lists basic descriptive statistics (N, mean, standard deviation, minimum, and maximum) for air temperature.
   b. Convert the code from part a) into a macro that will produce either the frequency report or the descriptive statistics report based on a value of a parameter that is passed to the macro.
   c. Add a parameter to the macro that can control which variable is used for the report.

    d.   Add a title that reflects the type of report (frequency or descriptive statistics) with a short description of the variable. Specify the description of the variable as a parameter for the macro.

    e.   Call the macro for each of the variables Month, Warning, AirTemp, and WindSpeed. Choose the appropriate type of report for each variable.

23. The United States Department of Transportation publishes statistics on many modes of transportation. The SAS data set called AIRTRAFFIC contains data on the number of flights and passengers leaving 12 major airports in the United States. The data set contains data from each airline, for each quarter, for 20 years. In addition to the variables for year, quarter, and airline, there are two variables representing number of flights and passengers for each of the 12 airports. The variable names for the flights and passengers all start with the three-letter airport code: ATL (Atlanta), BOS (Boston), DEN (Denver), DFW (Dallas Fort Worth), EWR (Newark), HNL (Honolulu), LAX (Los Angeles), MIA (Miami), ORD (Chicago), SAN (San Diego), SEA (Seattle), and SFO (San Francisco). The data are sorted by year, airline, and quarter.

    a.   Examine this SAS data set including the variable labels and attributes. For BOS (Boston), create a data set that contains variables for the sum of the flights and for the sum of the passengers over all quarters, for each airline for one selected year of your choice. Use a macro variable to specify the value of the selected year.

    b.   Use the data set from part a) to create another data set with one observation for the airline with the most passengers for the selected year. Create a variable that represents the number of passengers per flight for that one year and airline. Round this value to a whole number.

    c.   Convert your code for parts a) and b) into a macro so that it can be run for any airport. Call the macro once for each of the 12 airports.

    d.   Combine the 12 data sets containing the airline with the most passengers generated in part c) into a data set with one observation for each airport.

    e.   Print the data set from part d) including variables for the airport code, airline name, total flights, total passengers, and the number of passengers per flight. Include the selected year in the title for the report.

    f.   Incorporate additional macro programming that will enable you to calculate the statistics on the 12 airports and run the report for a range of years of your choice.

24. Suppose that at a local university the study guidelines for the College of Science and Math are to study two to three hours per unit per week. The instructor of the class, Orientation to the Statistics Major, takes these guidelines very seriously. He asks students to record their study time each week and then he runs a report to monitor their progress. The SAS data set called STUDYTIME contains student identification information, orientation course-section number, number of units enrolled, and time studied for the final week of classes.

a. Examine this SAS data set including the variable labels and attributes. Create a variable that calculates the time studied per unit for each student.
b. Use the variable from part a) to calculate the average time studied per unit per section. Output these statistics to a data set.
c. Create a macro that will print the data for all students in a specified section. Include the section number in the title.
d. Specify an option that will enable you to see the values of the macro variables as details in the log.
e. Create a footnote based on the average time studied per unit per section from part b). If the section average meets the minimum two hours of study time, the footnote should state that the average study time was met for the section. For a section average that is less than the minimum study time, the footnote should state that the average was not met. Add this footnote to the report.
f. Include programming that will add the calculated section average time from part b) to the footnote. Round the average time to two decimal places.
g. Call the macro once for each section.
h. If you used DATA step programming for parts e), f), and g), then repeat these parts using PROC SQL. Otherwise, repeat these parts using DATA step methods.

25. Suppose that you have mortgage application data from a national bank with five branches in California contained in a SAS data set called LOANAPP. The Board of Directors would like some information about the loans for the higher-priced properties. Variables in this data set include the identification information for the applicant, credit score, loan information, home price, and the down payment as a percent of the sales price.

a. Examine this SAS data set including the variable labels and attributes. Compute the mean credit score, interest rate, and down payment percentage for approved loans. Limit the loans used in the calculations to primary residential properties with sale prices over $800,000.
b. Convert the code from part a) to a macro with parameters for the property type and sales price limit. Call the macro once for each of the four property types using the following limits: residential properties with sale prices over $800,000, secondary residential properties over $800,000, investment or rental properties over $1,000,000, and commercial properties over $1,200,000.
c. Modify the macro to produce the means for the same variables for each of the five branches for primary residential properties, and overall means for the other property types. Call the macro again for each property type. Use an option that will enable you to see the standard SAS statements generated by each macro call.
d. Create one data set containing all the means from part c). The data set should have five observations for primary residential properties (one for each branch) and three more observations for the overall means for the other three property types described in part c). Include variables for the property type and for the cutoff used for sale price for properties used in the calculations.

e.   Produce a report using the results of part d). Format the data values appropriately, and label the variables where necessary.

26. Debugging macros can be tedious, but using SAS system options for debugging macros can help by turning on certain messages that are written to the log. Consider the following SAS program that creates a times table for any dimensions specified, in this case 12 by 12.

```
%MACRO tt (NumRows=,NumCols=);
   DATA table (DROP = &NumRows &NumCols);
      ARRAY col(&NumCols) col1 - col&NumCols;
      DO i = 1 TO "&NumRows";
         DO j = 1 TO "&NumCols";
            col(j) = i * j;
         END;
         OUTPUT;
      END;
   RUN;

PROC PRINT DATA = TABLE;
      TITLE1 'Times Table Printed for';
      TITLE2 '&NumRows by &NumCols';
      TITLE3 "Printed on &sysdate";
   RUN;
%MEND tt;

%tt(NumRows = 12,NumCols = 12)
```

a.   Type this program into the editor and submit it.

b.   Review the log for any errors and warnings, or any notes that indicate that SAS may have tried to fix your program for you. Add a comment to your program about the messages that you found in the log.

c.   Add two options to your program so that the log will display the standard code that is generated by macros and the values of the macro variables.

d.   Run the program again and review the log. Add a comment to your program that identifies and explains the issues identified in part b). Discuss how the code can be changed to prevent the issues identified in these log messages.

e.   Fix the issues that you identified in part d). Review the titles in the output. Add a comment to your program that identifies if the title looks different from what was intended and explain why this occurred.

CHAPTER 8

Visualizing Your Data

Multiple Choice

1. ODS Graphics does which of the following?

    a. It can send graphs to the LISTING destination
    b. It enables statistical procedures to produce graphics
    c. It uses ODS style templates
    d. All of the above

2. Which types of plots can be overlaid together in a single graph?

    a. box and scatter
    b. loess and density
    c. scatter and series
    d. histogram and bar

3. The STYLE= option can go in which statement in order to specify a style template for a graph?

    a. ODS HTML
    b. ODS GRAPHICS
    c. PROC SGPLOT
    d. None of the above

4. A stacked bar chart based on the variables Year and Type can be created with which of the following statements?

   a. `VBAR Year / GROUP = Type;`
   b. `VBAR Year / GROUP = Type GROUPDISPLAY = STACK;`
   c. `HBAR Year / GROUP = Type;`
   d. All of the above

5. Which statement will draw a normal curve in PROC SGPLOT?

   a. `HISTOGRAM Age / DENSITY;`
   b. `DENSITY Age;`
   c. `HISTOGRAM Age / NORMAL;`
   d. `NORMAL Age;`

6. Which of the following will tell SAS to create box plots as separate graphs for each level of a categorical variable named Origin?

   a. CATEGORY = Origin
   b. GROUP = Origin
   c. BY Origin
   d. All of the above

7. You can produce a fitted line on a scatter plot with which SGPLOT statement?

   a. SCATTER
   b. SERIES
   c. REG
   d. All of the above

8. You can create a scatter plot with labels on the data points that represent the Y axis values with which of the following statements?

   a. `SCATTER X = MSRP Y = Invoice;`
   b. `SCATTER X = MSRP Y = Invoice / DATALABEL = Invoice;`
   c. `SCATTER X = MSRP Y = Invoice / DATALABEL = YAXIS;`
   d. All of the above

9. Which of the following is an option that will automatically place reference lines at each tick mark?

    a. REFLINE
    b. GRID
    c. VALUES=
    d. None of the above

10. How can you tell SAS to replace the variable name on an axis with a label?

    a. Use an XAXIS statement with a LABEL= option
    b. Specify a LABEL statement in the DATA step
    c. Use a LABEL statement in PROC SGPLOT
    d. All of the above

11. What will happen if you specify TRANSPARENCY = 1 in a plot statement in PROC SGPLOT?

    a. Transparency will be turned on
    b. Transparency will be turned off
    c. The plot feature will be dark
    d. The plot feature will disappear

12. What is true about legends?

    a. They only appear when using the KEYLEGEND statement
    b. They cannot appear if there is an inset
    c. Placement can be controlled with a KEYLEGEND statement
    d. All legends have borders

13. Which option could be used to modify the data points on a scatter plot?

    a. FILLATTRS=
    b. LINEATTRS=
    c. MARKERATTRS=
    d. None of the above

14. Which of the following is not true about the SGPANEL procedure?

    a. It uses nearly all the same plot statements as PROC SGPLOT
    b. It requires a BY statement
    c. It produces multi-celled graphs
    d. It requires at least one categorical variable

15. What ODS GRAPHICS statement option will tell SAS to give an image file a specific name every time the code is run?

   a.   RESET
   b.   IMAGENAME=
   c.   Both of the above used together
   d.   Neither of the above

Short Answer

16. What is the main difference between graphs that are automatically created by ODS Graphics versus graphs created using PROC SGPLOT?

17. Suppose you use a VBAR and HISTOGRAM statement together inside the same SGPLOT procedure. Would SAS be able to create a graph with this combination of statements? Explain why or why not.

18. Suppose a student combines a histogram with a normal density plot, but the histogram appears on top of the density plot, which makes it hard to see. Explain what went wrong and at least one way this can this be fixed.

19. When you use a SERIES statement in PROC SGPLOT, the X axis data must be organized in the correct order. Explain what can go wrong if the data are not organized properly and how this can be fixed.

20. The SERIES and REG statements both have an option to turn the markers on and off. However, the SCATTER statement does not have this ability. Explain why this makes sense.

21. What are the similarities and differences between the SIZE= and THICKNESS= attributes?

22. Describe the graphics file that SAS would create if you submit the following statements along with PROC SGPLOT. Explain what would happen if you resubmit the code.

```
ODS LISTING GPATH = 'c:\GraphicFiles'
    STYLE = ANALYSIS;

ODS GRAPHICS / IMAGENAME = 'Weather'
    OUTPUTFMT = PNG HEIGHT = 4IN WIDTH = 6IN;
```

Programming Exercises

23. The *World Bank* works internationally with the goal of reducing poverty. Their website tracks population by country. The SAS data set called POPULATION contains data on the estimated number of residents (in 100,000s) of various countries by year.

    a. Examine this SAS data set including the variable labels and attributes. Create a histogram of the most recent population estimates for all countries combined.
    b. Create separate histograms of the most recent population estimates for each continent.
    c. Create a single graph with box plots of the most recent population estimates per continent.
    d. In a comment in your program, describe the main differences between the statistical information that can be visualized in the histograms from part b) compared to the box plots from part c).

24. A study on weight loss in males was conducted over a five-month period. Participants came to a clinic at the beginning of each month, and their weight as well as their responses to six survey questions regarding weight loss were obtained. The SAS data set called WLS contains variables for subject ID, height (in), weight (lb), and body mass index (BMI) at the baseline visit, and responses to six questions at each of five visits for a total of 30 survey questions. Note that the first six survey questions are from visit one, the next six survey questions are from visit two, and so on.

    a. Examine this SAS data set including the variable labels and attributes. Create a bar chart of the responses to the first survey question from visit one. Include a bar for missing values and label it as Missing.
    b. Create another bar chart of the responses to the first survey question from visit one, and this time summarize the average BMI so that each bar represents the average BMI for all people with the response.
    c. Include standard error limit lines on the bars for the graph from part b). Include a bar for missing values and label it as Missing.
    d. On your graph from parts b) and c), limit the range of the Y axis to meaningful values of average BMI (15 to 30). Label BMI as Mean Body Mass Index.
    e. Using the same graph specifications as parts b), c), and d), create paneled graphs for the 30 survey questions. Make sure that the six questions corresponding to the same visit appear on the same graph.
    f. Inspect the paneled graph from part e). Re-create this graphic but include only the four survey questions having the most variation in average BMI among the 30 questions. Save an image of this graph as a stand-alone JPEG file using the ANALYSIS style.

25. The United States Patent and Trademark Office reports the number of utility patent grants (patents for inventions) per year. The American Community Survey reports selected social characteristics in the United States on geographic areas with a population of 65,000 or more. These data sources have been combined in a SAS data set called PATENTS that represents by county the number of patent grants, population estimate, and various demographic characteristics, for one year.

    a. Examine this SAS data set including the variable labels and attributes. Create a histogram of patent grants that includes a normal distribution overlay. Limit this plot to counties with 100 patents or more.
    b. Include a comment in your program that describes the shape of the histogram created in part a).
    c. Create a scatter plot of education versus patents. Limit this plot to counties with 100 or more patents.
    d. Add programming to identify the county with the largest number of patents by including the name of that one county as a label on the scatter plot created in part c).
    e. Modify the markers on the scatter plot from parts c) and d) so that they are filled circles with 50% transparency.

26. The United States Geological Survey provides data on earthquakes of historical interest. The SAS data set called EARTHQUAKES contains data about earthquakes with a magnitude greater than 2.5 in the United States and its territories. The variables are year, month, day, state, and magnitude.

    a. Examine this SAS data set including the variable labels and attributes. Create a scatter plot of year and magnitude for earthquakes that occurred in the year 2000 and beyond.
    b. Overlay a time series plot of the mean magnitude for each year on the same graph as part a). This line should appear in red on your graph.
    c. Include a legend for your graph that labels the time series plot as Mean. The legend should have no border and appear on the bottom right side of the plot.
    d. Earthquakes are classified by their magnitude. Overlay reference lines on your graph for light, moderate, strong, major, and great earthquakes defined at magnitudes of 4.0, 5.0, 6.0, 7.0, and 8.0, respectively. These lines should be labeled, dashed, and have 50% transparency.
    e. Make sure that all years appear on the X axis of your graph.

27. Suppose that at a local university the study guidelines for the College of Science and Math are to study two to three hours per unit per week. The instructor of the class, Orientation to the Statistics Major, takes these guidelines very seriously. He asks students to record their study time each week, and at the end of the term he compares their average study time per week to their term GPA. The SAS data set called STUDY_GPA contains student identification information, orientation course-section number, number of units enrolled, average time studied, and term GPA.

   a. Examine this SAS data set including the variable labels and attributes. Create box plots to compare the time studied between the two sections.
   b. Create a simple linear regression plot for time studied and GPA. Turn off the legend.
   c. Create a simple linear regression plot for time studied and GPA with a line for each section. Move the legend to the far right side of the plot.
   d. Add 95% confidence limits for the mean predicted values to your plot from part c). Adjust the transparency so that bands for both sections are visible on the plot.
   e. Add a comment to your program about any potential relationships that you see between the variables included on these three plots.

28. The United States Department of Transportation publishes data on air travel in the United States. The SAS data set called AIRLINES contains 20 years' worth of data for 12 major airlines. The variables include year, airline, airport code, number of flights and passengers, and tons of freight and mail departing from selected United States airports. The data set also contains a variable for the size of the airport categorized as small, medium, or large.

   a. Examine this SAS data set including the variable labels and attributes. Create a data set with the total number of passengers for each combination of airline, airport size, and year.
   b. Using the data set from part a), create one series plot for each airline showing the total number of passengers per year for each year. Show separate lines for small, medium, and large airports.
   c. Create the same plots as for part b), but instead of having one graph for each airline, group the plots so that you have two paneled graphs with the data for six airlines displayed in each graph. Eliminate any unnecessary labeling in the cell headings for the airlines.
   d. Modify the Y axis in part c) so that the tick marks are presented in millions. Label the Y axis appropriately.
   e. There have been a number of airline mergers over the 20-year period. In 2006, America West Airlines started being reported under US Airways, and, in 2010, Northwest Airlines started being reported under Delta Air Lines. Re-create the graphic from parts c) and d) and add text inside the plot area for US Airways and Delta Air Lines noting the year and change in airline name.

CHAPTER 9

Using Basic Statistical Procedures

Multiple Choice

1. To carry out a normality test, which procedure could you use?

    a. FREQ
    b. UNIVARIATE
    c. Both
    d. Neither

2. Which procedure will display the median by default?

    a. TTEST
    b. MEANS
    c. UNIVARIATE
    d. All of the above

3. In which procedure can you choose to display only the mean, median, and standard deviation in the results?

    a. TTEST
    b. MEANS
    c. UNIVARIATE
    d. None of the above

4. Which procedure can compute a one-sample *t* test against any desired hypothesized value?

    a. TTEST
    b. MEANS
    c. Both
    d. Neither

5. Which procedure can compute a paired *t* test of any difference on paired data stored as differences in one column?

    a. TTEST
    b. MEANS
    c. Both
    d. Neither

6. It is not possible to produce which of the following plot types using PROC TTEST?

    a. Bar charts
    b. Histograms
    c. Box plots
    d. Quantile-Quantile plots

7. Which procedure can produce descriptive statistics for both character and numeric data?

    a. TTEST
    b. MEANS
    c. FREQ
    d. None of the above

8. Chi-square tests can be computed using which procedure?

    a. FREQ
    b. UNIVARIATE
    c. CORR
    d. None of the above

9. Which plot is created by default for a one-way chi-square test?

    a. AGREEPLOT
    b. CUMFREQPLOT
    c. DEVIATIONPLOT
    d. FREQPLOT

10. How many different correlations will be calculated with the following PROC CORR?

    ```
    PROC CORR DATA = lines;
      VAR CR25 CR75 M25 M75;
      WITH GPA;
    RUN;
    ```

    a. 4
    b. 5
    c. 8
    d. 10

11. PROC CORR can produce which of the following plot types?

    a. Fit plots
    b. Density curves
    c. Box plots
    d. Scatter plots

12. Which MODEL statement will correctly specify a simple linear regression model with the variable Age predicting the variable Sales?

    a. `MODEL Age = Sales;`
    b. `MODEL Sales = Age;`
    c. `MODEL Age * Sales;`
    d. `MODEL Sales * Age;`

13. In a simple linear regression model with one dependent variable and one independent variable, which plot will not be part of the diagnostic panel?

    a. A fit plot
    b. A residual plot against the predicted values
    c. Cook's D by observation number
    d. A normal plot of the residuals

14. A MODEL statement is required by which procedure?

    a. REG
    b. ANOVA
    c. Both
    d. Neither

15. A CLASS statement is required by which procedure?

    a.   MEANS
    b.   TTEST
    c.   REG
    d.   ANOVA

16. What is a reason to include the MEANS statement in PROC ANOVA?

    a.   To create a side-by-side box plot to compare the means of each group
    b.   To perform pairwise comparisons of groups
    c.   To generate the analysis of variance table to test the overall mean differences
    d.   To define the grouping variable

Short Answer

17. You would like to carry out a paired t test to compare the difference in mean heart rate before and after treatment. The data set that you are given contains only one variable that represents the difference between the two measurements. Which procedures and accompanying statements could enable you to carry out this test with this data set? Explain your choices.

18. You would like to carry out a hypothesis test to compare the average GPA of males and females for students in the College of Science and Math at your university. Your data set includes one observation for each student with GPA stored as one variable and gender stored as another variable. Besides the PROC and RUN statements, which two additional statements would be required to accomplish this with one PROC TTEST? Be specific about which variable goes with each statement.

19. Suppose you would like to carry out a hypothesis test to look for an association between student gender and college of major (Liberal Studies, Engineering, and so on) at your university. Your data set includes one observation for each student with gender stored as one variable and college of major stored as another variable. What procedure and options do you need to accomplish this?

20. Explain why it makes sense that PROC UNIVARIATE will create a histogram and PROC FREQ will create bar charts.

21. When using the PLOTS = MATRIX(HISTOGRAM) option in PROC CORR, histograms are displayed along the diagonal in a correlation matrix. Explain why these histograms are useful and what they represent.

22. Explain the importance of including the diagnostics panel in simple linear regression output.

23. What is the purpose of the MEANS statement in the following code? Be specific.

```
PROC ANOVA DATA = sasdata.magazine;
   CLASS Mag;
   MODEL Wds = Mag;
   MEANS Mag / SCHEFFE;
RUN;
```

Programming Exercises

24. Each year, *Forbes* magazine publishes a list of the world's 100 biggest companies. Each company receives a score using four metrics: sales, profits, assets, and market value. The final overall ranking is based on a composite score of these metrics. The SAS data set called BIGCOMP includes variables for ranking, company name, and these four metrics.

    a. Examine this SAS data set including the variable labels and attributes. Use a procedure to calculate the mean, standard deviation, median, minimum, maximum, and sample size of assets for United States versus non-United States companies.
    b. Use a different procedure to calculate the same statistics as in part a).

25. A study was conducted to see whether taking vitamin E daily would reduce the levels of atherosclerotic disease in a random sample of 500 individuals. Clinical measurements, including thickness of plaque of the carotid artery (taken via ultrasound), were recorded at baseline and at two subsequent visits in a SAS data set called VITE. Patients were divided into two strata according to their baseline plaque measurement.

    a. Examine this SAS data set including the variable labels and attributes. Is there evidence to suggest that the true mean systolic blood pressure at baseline is significantly greater than 140 mm/Mg? Carry out an appropriate hypothesis test for each strata, and compare the resulting p-values to alpha = 0.05.
    b. You would like to test for differences in true mean plaque before treatment and at the second-year visit. Examine the layout of the data set, and in a comment describe why this data set structure would not work for the hypothesis test that you need to use.
    c. Test for a difference in plaque as specified in part b) for the treatment group and also for the placebo group. Carry out appropriate hypothesis tests for each strata, and compare the resulting p-values to alpha = 0.05.
    d. To complete the analysis, compare the differences that you saw in mean plaque before and at the second-year visit across the two treatment groups. Carry out appropriate hypothesis tests for each strata, and compare the resulting p-values to alpha = 0.05.
    e. Verify the assumption of normality for the tests in parts c) and d). Include plots as well as p-values.
    f. In a comment in your program, discuss the results from parts c) and d).

26. Researchers conducted a study of left-handedness in a random sample of elementary school aged children and stored their results in a SAS data set called LEFTIES. They collected data on the hand preference for writing, cutting with scissors, and using a mouse. Data were also collected on the foot that the child used to kick a ball, as well as age and gender.

    a. Examine this SAS data set including the variable labels and attributes. Is there an association between writing hand and kicking foot preference? Carry out the appropriate hypothesis test and compare the resulting p-value to alpha = 0.05.
    b. Is there an association between writing hand and mousing hand preference? Carry out the appropriate hypothesis test and compare the resulting p-value to alpha = 0.05.
    c. Is there an association between writing hand and gender? Carry out the appropriate hypothesis test and compare the resulting p-value to alpha = 0.05.
    d. Create bar charts to accompany each of the tests in parts a), b), and c).
    e. In a comment in your program, discuss the results and any concerns that you might have about the expected cell count assumption for these tests.

27. The SAS data set called APTEST contains data compiled from the College Board for all states participating in the High School Advanced Placement exam for Computer Science (AP CS A) in a single year. These data present passing rates overall, for females only, for African Americans, and for Hispanics. In addition, data from the United States Census Annual Survey of School System Finances regarding per pupil spending in elementary and secondary school systems by state were combined with these exam results.

    a. Examine this SAS data set including the variable labels and attributes. Calculate the correlation between total percentage of students passing and total spending per pupil. Limit this analysis to states with at least one student taking the exam.
    b. In a comment in your program, discuss the results from part a) comparing the resulting p-value to alpha = 0.05. Why is the sample size lower than expected?
    c. Calculate correlations for all of the AP exam variables (these are the second through ninth variables in the data set) and the census spending variables (these are the last 11 variables in the data set). Format the correlation table such that AP exam results represent the rows, and the census spending variables represent the columns. Limit this analysis to states with at least one student taking the exam.
    d. Review the results from part c) to identify the two variables with the strongest correlation. Perform a simple linear regression analysis using the census spending variable as the independent variable and the AP exam variable as the dependent variable. Limit this analysis to states with at least one student taking the exam.
    e. Make sure that your analysis from part d) includes a fitted line plot. Are there any observations that appear to be extreme in both their X and Y values? Record the state name and the X and Y values of any such observations as a comment in your program.
    f. To examine the impact of extreme observations on the analysis, repeat part d) excluding any extreme observations identified in part e). In a comment in your program, record the slope of the regression line and the R-squared value for both models.

28. The United States Patent and Trademark Office reports the number of utility patent grants (patents for inventions) per year. The American Community Survey reports selected social characteristics in the United States on geographic areas with a population of 65,000 or more. These data sources have been combined in a SAS data set called PATENTS that represents by county the number of patent grants, population estimate, and various demographic characteristics, for one year.

    a. Examine this SAS data set including the variable labels and attributes. Test to see whether there is a linear relationship between education and number of patents, comparing the resulting p-value to alpha = 0.05. Limit this test to counties with 100 or more patents.
    b. In a comment in your program, discuss the results and any concerns that you might have about the assumptions of normality and constant variance of the residuals for the test from part a). Identify any extreme observations.
    c. Calculate the base 10 log of the variables from part a), and repeat the test using the transformed values.
    d. In a comment in your program, discuss the results and any concerns that you might have about the assumptions of normality and constant variance of the residuals for the test from part c).
    e. Output the data used to create the residual plot for part c) to a data set, and use this to calculate a test of normality for the residuals comparing the resulting p-value to alpha = 0.05.
    f. Include a comment in your program about the results from part e).
    g. Convert your analysis to a simple macro using a parameter to pass in the independent variable. Add titles with the dependent and independent variable names, and name the output data set for the residuals differently for each independent variable. Call the macro twice using independent variables of your choice.
    h. Create a PDF file that contains the results of your entire analysis.

29. The local public transportation company would like to conduct a study of the impact of three possible plans on a certain popular bus route in town. Plan one consists of traffic lights timed in sync via a special remote transmitter on the bus that interacts with the traffic signal. Plan two consists of shutting down a regular traffic lane to become an express lane for buses only. Plan three is the current normal bus route with no changes. To assess the impact of a change, the company implemented plan one for a month, and then implemented plan two for a different month. All three plans were measured during summer months to ensure consistency in weather. The time (in minutes) for a bus to complete its route was measured for randomly selected weekdays and weekends, and these data are stored in the SAS data set called BUS.

    a. Examine this SAS data set including the variable labels and attributes. Calculate the mean, median, and standard deviation travel time for each plan. Present these descriptive statistics to one decimal place.
    b. Test to see whether there is any difference between the mean times for any of the plans, and compare the resulting p-value to alpha = 0.05.

c.   Add pairwise comparisons of group means to the analysis from part b).

d.   In a comment in your program, discuss your findings. Which plan should the city adopt?

CHAPTER 10

Exporting Your Data

Multiple Choice

1. Most software applications can read what file format?

    a. CSV
    b. XML
    c. RTF
    d. JMP

2. Which of the following export methods will enable you to create a CSV file?

    a. DATA step
    b. PROC EXPORT
    c. ODS with a PROC PRINT
    d. All of the above

3. Which of the following export methods can export formatted data values to a delimited file?

    a. DATA step
    b. PROC EXPORT
    c. ODS with a PROC PRINT
    d. All of the above

4.   How can you assign formats to data in CSV files exported with PROC EXPORT?

   a.   With a FORMAT statement in PROC EXPORT
   b.   With a FORMAT statement in a DATA step before PROC EXPORT
   c.   By including PROC FORMAT before PROC EXPORT
   d.   Using the REPLACE option in PROC EXPORT

5.   Which PROC EXPORT option cannot be used to specify a file type?

   a.   DELIMITER=
   b.   OUTFILE=
   c.   DBMS=
   d.   None of the above

6.   Which of the following export methods can save procedure results as a delimited file without first creating a SAS data set?

   a.   DATA step
   b.   PROC EXPORT
   c.   ODS
   d.   All of the above

7.   Which ODS destination will exclude titles and footnotes?

   a.   CSV
   b.   CSVALL
   c.   HTML
   d.   RTF

8.   Which of the following is not specified in the ODS EXCEL statement?

   a.   Naming an Excel worksheet
   b.   Embedding titles on a worksheet
   c.   Turning on autofiltering
   d.   Representing missing numeric data with null values rather than a period

9.   The EXPORT procedure will not allow you to do which of the following?

   a.   Create Microsoft Excel files with multiple sheets
   b.   Create multiple Microsoft Excel files with one PROC EXPORT
   c.   Create delimited files using * as the delimiter
   d.   Create tab delimited files

10. Which of the following cannot be incorporated into a raw data file created with the DATA step?

   a. Text strings
   b. Formats
   c. Bold font
   d. Comma delimiters

Short Answer

11. What are the main differences between exporting a delimited file with the PROC EXPORT versus with the DATA step?

12. Explain why it might be important to include double quotation marks around character data in a CSV file.

Programming Exercises

13. The SAS data set called CARTALK contains information regarding episodes of the automotive repair radio talk show *Car Talk*. Variables in this data set include episode number, air date, title, and a description of the show.

   a. Examine this SAS data set including the variable labels and attributes. Create a CSV file from the SAS data set using ODS and PROC PRINT.
   b. Add PROC EXPORT code to create another CSV file. Give this data file a different filename from the data file created in part a).
   c. Add code to create another CSV file using a DATA step. Give this data file a different filename from the data files created in parts a) and b).
   d. Open the three CSV files and compare them. In a comment in your program, discuss any differences or similarities.
   e. Compare the code used to generate the three CSV files. In a comment in your program, discuss any differences or similarities.

14. The *World Bank* works internationally with the goal of reducing poverty. Their website tracks many financial indicators across countries. The SAS data set called EXCHANGERATE contains data on the average exchange rate (relative to United States dollars) for recent time periods.

   a. Examine this SAS data set including the variable labels and attributes. Use PROC EXPORT to create a Microsoft Excel file that contains the observations with missing data in the most recent time period. Name this worksheet Recent Missing.
   b. Format the exchange rate data so that it includes commas where appropriate.

c.   Add worksheets to the Microsoft Excel file created in part a) for each of the seven continents, using their full names as the name of each worksheet. Exclude any observations that already appear on the Recent Missing worksheet.

d.   Create a similar Excel file for parts a), b), and c) using ODS.

e.   Open the two Excel files and compare them. In a comment in your program, discuss any differences or similarities.

15.   The advising center at the local university schedules one mandatory advising appointment during the junior year for every student. The purpose of this appointment is to ensure that the student is on track for graduation. The SAS data set called ADVISING contains data for the current junior class with variables for student name, an identification number, and the advising appointment date. Do not modify the values of any of the variables in the data set to create the following.

a.   Examine this SAS data set including the variable labels and attributes. Create a raw data file that is space-delimited. This file should contain the data for the appointment date, first name, last name, and identification number, in this order.

b.   Organize the raw data file so that students with no appointment date appear first in the file, followed by those with appointment dates listed in chronological order. Within each appointment date, students should be arranged by identification number.

c.   Missing appointment dates should be represented by XX/XX/XXXX in the raw data file. Nonmissing appointment dates should be represented using a similar format.

d.   For the first name, only the first initial should appear in the raw data file.

16.   The SAS data set called APTEST contains data from the College Board for all states participating in the High School Advanced Placement exam for Computer Science (AP CS A) in a single year. These data present passing rates overall, for females only, for African Americans, and for Hispanics. In addition, data from the United States Census Annual Survey of School System Finances regarding per pupil spending in elementary and secondary school systems by state were combined with these exam results.

a.   Examine this SAS data set including the variable labels and attributes. Use ODS statements to create an Excel file. The file should contain data for the state, number of schools, total percent passing, female percent passing, per pupil elementary-secondary spending, and per pupil salary and wages, in this order. Use the variable labels as column headings.

b.   Do not include observation numbers or a title in the Excel data file.

c.   Present missing numeric data as blanks. Format the spending and salary/wages data as dollars to two decimal places.

CHAPTER 11

Debugging Your SAS Programs

Multiple Choice

1. Using the FIRSTOBS= and OBS= options will control the number of lines of raw data read by which statement?

   a. INFILE
   b. SET
   c. PROC PRINT
   d. All of the above

2. Writing programs that are easy to read will make your code easier to debug. Which of the following is not just a simple habit that you can use to make programs easier to read?

   a. Placing each statement on a new line
   b. Indenting statements within DATA and PROC steps
   c. Using DO and END statements
   d. Using comments in your program

3. Which type of log message will prevent your program from running?

   a. Errors
   b. Warnings
   c. Notes
   d. All of the above

4.   Which option will tell SAS to read in all the observations in your data set?

    a.   OBS = 0
    b.   OBS = N
    c.   OBS = MAX
    d.   OBS = _ALL_

5.   When SAS encounters a syntax error, what is displayed in the log?

    a.   An error message
    b.   The possible location of the error
    c.   An explanation of the error
    d.   All of the above

6.   A missing semicolon can cause which of the following to happen?

    a.   Two SAS statements will be concatenated
    b.   Confusing warnings
    c.   A variety of error messages
    d.   All of the above

7.   What might cause SAS go to the next line when trying to read in raw data?

    a.   An INFILE statement with the TRUNCOVER option
    b.   An INFILE statement with the MISSOVER option
    c.   Raw data that uses / as the delimiter
    d.   Raw data lines that are shorter than what is expected from informats specified in the INPUT statement

8.   A lost-card note indicates what problem?

    a.   SAS thinks your raw data file is incomplete
    b.   SAS thinks your INPUT statement is incomplete
    c.   You have invalid data
    d.   A character variable has been truncated

9.   An invalid-data note in the log might indicate what type of problem?

    a.   A missing semicolon in the DATA step
    b.   Misspelling the name for a numeric variable
    c.   Forgetting to include a dollar sign for a character variable in the INPUT statement
    d.   Using column input to read character data with embedded blanks

10. When would SAS produce a missing-values-were-generated note?

    a.　When SAS goes to the next line to look for raw data
    b.　When SAS encounters a blank line in the raw data file
    c.　With a raw data file that does not include periods for missing numeric data
    d.　When adding two numeric variables that have at least one missing value

11. The following note could be prevented by using what function?

    ```
    NOTE:   Character values have been converted to
            numeric values at the places given by:
    (Line):(Column).
            789:3
    ```

    a.　INPUT
    b.　PUT
    c.　INFILE
    d.　FILE

12. Which of the following would cause SAS to convert a character variable to numeric?

    a.　Using a PUT function
    b.　Performing a mathematical expression using a character variable
    c.　Including a numeric variable in a SUBSTR function
    d.　All of the above

13. Which SAS statement will print values of variables to the log in any DATA step?

    a.　PUT
    b.　PUTLOG
    c.　PRINTLOG
    d.　LOG

14. Which error message indicates that you may have misspelled a keyword?

    a.　Invalid-option-name
    b.　Invalid-data
    c.　Lost-card
    d.　None of the above

15. Misspelling a variable name in the expression of an assignment statement will produce what type of log message?

    a. A statement-is-not-valid message
    b. An invalid-data note
    c. An invalid-option message
    d. A variable-is-uninitialized note

16. What is the length of the variable X in the resulting SAS data set called WATER?

    ```
    DATA water;
      SET fresh (KEEP = Y);
      IF Y < 2 THEN X = 'Purified';
        ELSE X = 'Distilled';
      LENGTH X $ 10;
    RUN;
    ```

    a. 10
    b. 9
    c. 8
    d. No data set is created due to syntax errors in the program

17. What is the length of the variable Group in the resulting SAS data set called STATUS?

    ```
    DATA status;
      INFILE 'c:\MyRawData\info.dat' TRUNCOVER;
      INPUT Age Group $ 10-19;
      IF Age < 15 THEN Group = 'Low';
        ELSE IF 15 <= Age < 25 THEN Group = 'Medium';
        ELSE IF 25 <= Age THEN Group = 'High';
    RUN;
    ```

    a. 3
    b. 4
    c. 6
    d. 10

18. Which SAS statement will help you reduce the size of your data set by limiting it to only the observations of interest?

    a. LENGTH
    b. Subsetting IF
    c. SET
    d. COMPRESS

19. Which SAS option will help you reduce the size of your data set by limiting it to only the variables of interest?

    a. WHERE=
    b. OBS=
    c. KEEP=
    d. FIRSTOBS=

Short Answer

20. Verifying the accuracy of the SAS data sets that you create is an important step. For a very large data set, PROC PRINT may not be the best option. Identify another procedure that may be helpful for examining the accuracy of data values when you have many observations. Explain your choice.

21. Consider the following SAS log. Identify the mistake in the program and describe why the mistake causes each of the messages in the log.

```
1       DATA new;
2          INPUT A B C
3          DATALINES;
4       1 2 3
        _
        180
ERROR 180-322: Statement is not valid or it is
          used out of proper order.

5       4 5 6
6       3 6 9
7       ;
8       RUN;

ERROR: No DATALINES or INFILE statement.

NOTE: The SAS System stopped processing this step
          because of errors.

WARNING: The data set WORK.NEW may be incomplete.
             When this step was stopped there were 0
             observations and 4 variables.
```

22. When reading multiple lines of raw data for each observation, SAS may generate a lost-card note if there are missing or duplicate lines. Describe which observations will appear in the resulting SAS data set, and why a lost-card note in the log is important.

23. Suppose SAS reports the (line):(column) information in a message in your log. What does this information tell you and why is it important?

24. Explain why the location of the PUTLOG statement in a DATA step is important for debugging.

25. Consider the following SAS log. Identify the issue in the program and describe why the issue causes each of the messages in the log.

```
1 DATA vars;
2    SET new;
3    Total = A + B + C + D;
4 RUN;

NOTE: Variable D is uninitialized.

NOTE: Missing values were generated as a result
      of performing an operation on missing
      values.
      Each place is given by: (Number of
      times) at (Line):(Column).
      3 at 3:21
```

26. Explain how placing a LENGTH statement between the DATA and SET statements will enable you to modify the length of variables in an existing SAS data set.

Programming Exercises

27. A political candidate solicits donations through grassroots efforts via small house parties. After the house party, she records the donations to her campaign for each house. The raw data set called HouseParty.dat contains information on the most recent wave of house parties. The variables in this file are house ID, address, city, state, and ZIP code, followed by the name of each attendee and the amount donated at the house party.

    a. Open the raw data file in a simple editor such as WordPad. In a comment in your program, discuss why this data structure would be difficult to read into SAS with a single INPUT statement and without line pointers. What log messages might you encounter?

    b. Write a program that will read the raw data into SAS without errors or warnings in the log. The resulting SAS data set should have one observation per attendee with repeating house ID and address information for those at the same house party.

    c. Calculate the average amount donated by state. Make sure that states names are grouped together appropriately.

28. The local animal shelter maintains basic records about the animals available for adoption. The raw data file AnimalShelter.dat contains information about the shelter dogs: ID, breed, date when the dog was placed at the shelter, date of birth, gender, and status. Occasionally dates are not known or are incomplete. In this case, the animal shelter uses the code 99 for unknown information.

    a. After examining the raw data file, read AnimalShelter.dat into SAS without errors or warnings in the log.
    b. Adjust the intake date so that dates with a known month and year, but no day, use the 15th of the month.
    c. Calculate the age of the animal for those with a known date of birth.
    d. Create a format based on the values for status using the following coding scheme: 1 and 2 for transfers, 3 for strays, 4 and 5 for surrendered, and 6 for born at shelter.
    e. Apply the format created in part d) in a PUT function to create a character variable that represents the status grouping.
    f. For dogs not born at the shelter, create a report by status grouping that shows the number of observations with nonmissing age values and the mean, median, minimum, and maximum age. In addition, for all dogs, report the number of animals within each status grouping by breed of dog.
    g. Review the report created in part f) and identify any possible anomalies in the values of Age. Create an additional report that lists dogs with suspicious ages.

29. The United States Geological Survey provides data on earthquakes of historical interest. The SAS data set called EARTHQUAKES contains data about earthquakes with a magnitude greater than 2.5 in the United States and its territories. The variables are year, month, day, state, and magnitude. You assign a new employee the task of writing a program to create a data set with just the earthquakes from Alaska and then print the eruption date and magnitude for Alaskan earthquakes occurring in 2005 or later. The following is the program the new employee gives you.

    ```
    LIBNAME sasdata 'c:\MySASLib';

    DATA alaska (DROP = Year Month Day);
       SET sasdata.earthquakes;
       IF State = Alaska;
       EruptionDate = MDY(Month,Day,Year);
    RUN;

    PROC PRINT DATA = alaska NOROWNUM;
       WHERE Year GT 2005;
       VAR EruptionDate Magnitute;
       TITLE 'Alaska's Earthquakes in 2005 or Later';
       FORMAT EruptionDate DATE10.;
    RUN;
    ```

a.   Examine the SAS data set including the variable labels and attributes. Identify and correct any bugs in the preceding code so that this program will run correctly.

b.   Add comments to your revised program for each fix so that the new employee can understand her mistakes.

30. A local wireless mobile phone provider tracks monthly usage for all customers with plans that limit their usage by total number of minutes. The SAS data set called MOBILEDATA contains variables for the customer ID, plan limit (in minutes), and 12 months of mobile phone usage (in minutes). A recently hired analyst has written a SAS program to classify each month as under the minute limit, at the limit, or over the limit for the customer's plan. Unfortunately, his code does not work.

```
LIBNAME sasdata 'c:\MySASLib';

DATA compare (DROP = i);
  SET sasdata.mobiledata
  ARRAY mth(12) Month_1 - Month_12;
  ARRAY grp(12) $ Grp1 - Grp12;
  DO i = 1 TO 10;
    IF mth(i) < Minutes
              THEN grp(i) = Under;
      ELSE IF mth(i) = Minutes
              THEN grp(i) = At Plan Limit;
      ELSE IF mth(i) > Minutes
              THEN grp(i) = Over;
  END;
  AveMin = MEAN(Month_1 - Month_12);
RUN;
```

a.   Examine the SAS data set including the variable labels and attributes. Identify and correct the bugs in the preceding code so that this program will run correctly.

b.   Add comments to your revised program for each fix so that the analyst can understand his mistakes.

c.   Create a report that lists the ID, number of plan minutes, and average minutes for customers that exceed their limit every month.

31. An instructor at the local university teaches three sections of the same statistics course during the spring term and one section in the fall. The SAS data set called SPRINGGRADES has one observation per student for the spring term. The variables represent the course-section number, individual scores for each of the three exams, and a student ID. The SAS data set called FALLGRADES has the same information for the one section in the fall term. If a student did not take an exam, the score for that exam is missing.

a.   After examining the SAS data sets, and without altering them in any way, write a DATA step that simply stacks them into one new SAS data set. In a comment in your program, note any errors or warnings in your log and explain why the messages appear.

b. Create a new version of the FALLGRADES data set that fixes any issues identified in part a) that prevented it from being combined correctly with the SPRINGGRADES data set. Then combine the fixed version of the fall grades with the spring grades into one SAS data set so that the observations for the fall grades appear at the top of the new data set. Inspect the resulting data set to make sure that the variables were stacked correctly.

c. In a separate DATA step, combine the data sets from part b) again, only this time place the observations for the fall grades at the bottom of the data set. In a comment in your program, describe what happens to the course-section variable when you change the order of the data sets.

d. Add code to your program for part c) so that you will get the same result for the course-section variable no matter what order the data sets are combined.

e. In your program for part d) compute the final grade for each student by averaging the three exam score variables. If the student did not take an exam, then just take the average of the exams with scores.

f. Use the resulting data set from part e) to produce a report with the number of students, and the mean, standard deviation, minimum, and maximum final grade for each section.

PROJECTS

The projects in this chapter are designed to serve as a comprehensive capstone for the programming skills developed throughout the book. Each project gives you a chance to synthesize the material learned from various chapters. Completing a project may take several days of intense thought and coding and will result in a final product that could serve as evidence of SAS proficiency to a future employer or course instructor. Projects can be completed by a group or an individual.

Health and Human Services

The California Health and Human Services (CHHS) Agency Open Data Portal, found at www.chhs.ca.gov/, provides public access to health and human services information for the state of California. The goals of the Open Data Portal initiative include engaging the public in research and innovation activities. The Open Data Portal provides data by topic areas in tabular and graphical form. The user interface is simple to use and provides tools for filtering, visualizing, and exporting data. Many of the data sets available are fascinating. However, to include multiple data files in a single analysis will take some thought about which data are actually comparable and how to combine various data sets by a common variable.

a.   Research the current CHHS data that are available by topic area.
b.   Review the information available from at least three different categories in topic areas that you find interesting. Make sure that these data sources can be combined into one analysis by a common identifying variable, for example, county or year.

c. Based on your review, write a one-page research proposal that will examine relationships in the CHHS data across related topics. Describe the data files that will support your questions of interest, the appropriate variables, and statistics for your research questions. Describe how you plan to combine and manipulate the data sources into an analyzable data set.

d. Write a SAS program that reads in the CHHS data as they relate to your research proposal. Manipulate your data sets so that you can combine them into one data set to be used for analysis.

e. Carry out the appropriate analysis (descriptive statistics, graphics, and hypothesis tests) to investigate your research questions. Additionally, consider using macros whenever it makes sense to reduce the amount of repeated code.

f. Write a paper that summarizes the programming and analysis for this project. The paper should be no more than 12 pages with an abstract, an introduction, main topics and results, a conclusion, and references. Include relevant discussion and snippets of code that represent all parts of the project as well as a description of the analysis. Include your results and a discussion of the analysis with the appropriate statistics and figures to support your work.

Trends in the United States Census Data

Using the United States Census data provides an opportunity to work with real-life data that are current, interesting, large in scope, and challenging. The best place to start when becoming acquainted with the most recent United States Census is the main data web page at census.gov. This page lists interactive resources for searching and exporting the data as well as links that can take you to web pages for the raw data files. There are many Census data sets that are available ranging from the redistricting files, state demographic profiles, community surveys, geographic updates, and summary files. The release of the Census information is typically scheduled by product, at the state and national level.

The Census data files are available at the Census website in their raw form. However, getting the data into SAS becomes somewhat of a burden because the technical documentation needs to be deciphered and the programming needs to be written. There are several resources available online, not only from the Census Bureau, but also from other institutions (such as the Missouri Census Data Center) and from the SAS user community. These groups have worked toward making this information more easily available to others.

a. Research the most recent United States Census data and various sources that are available at the census.gov website. There are many useful resources for obtaining Census data such as web pages for finding populations and facts, an interactive map, and summary and redistricting files.

b. Review the technical documentation associated with the raw summary and redistricting files. Understanding how the raw data files are structured will help you decide which summary level is appropriate for your analysis.

c. Based on your review, write a one-page research proposal that will examine relationships in the Census data. Describe your questions of interest, the United States Census raw data files that will support your analysis, the appropriate summary level for your research questions, and your analytic plan.

d. Using SAS and your research proposal, carry out the appropriate analysis with the United States Census raw data files.

e. Write a paper that summarizes the programming and analysis for this project. The paper should be no more than 12 pages with an abstract, an introduction, main topics and results, a conclusion, and references. Include relevant discussion and snippets of code that represent all parts of the project as well as a description of the analysis. Include your results and a discussion of the analysis with the appropriate statistics and figures to support your work.

United States Federal Election Commission Donations

The Federal Election Commission (FEC) was established in 1975 to enforce the Federal Election Campaign Act. The FEC is an independent group that monitors campaign finance information, including limits on contributions and public funding of Presidential elections. The rules and make-up of the six-member committee encourages nonpartisan decisions. The FEC individual contributions data sets can be found at the FEC website (fec.gov). The data contain information on contributors who made donations, as well as refunds and transfers. Review the file format information to familiarize yourself with the layout of these files.

Consider which community characteristics might predict patterns in contributions made by individuals to a candidate for the most recent presidential primary, campaign, or election. Are there certain demographic characteristics of communities that are associated with how individuals contribute to presidential campaigns? For example, how much money or what proportion of contributions went to a certain political party or candidate? Review the available data sets (FEC data on individual contributions and the United States Census data) and develop research questions that you find plausible and interesting. There is a wealth of information in the Census and FEC contributions data, and not all of it needs to be used. But time should be invested to make sure that there are enough variables to complete a well thought out analysis.

a. Research the most recent United States Census data and various sources that are available at the census.gov website. There are many useful resources for obtaining Census data such as web pages for finding populations and facts, an interactive map, and summary and redistricting files.

b. Review the technical documentation associated with the raw summary and redistricting files. Understanding how the raw data files are structured will help you decide which summary level is appropriate for your analysis.

c. Write a one-page research proposal that investigates several associations between the United States Census data and the FEC contributions data. Include information to support your analysis, the appropriate summary level for your research questions, and an analytic plan.

d. Download the appropriate contributions data file from the FEC website. Write a SAS program that reads in the FEC contribution data as well as the relevant Census data. (Be careful to choose the correct summary level and relevant variables.) These programs should create data sets with only the pertinent variables that you have chosen for analysis.

e. Combine the SAS data sets that you created in part d) appropriately, in order to carry out your analysis. Be careful to research the difference between ZIP codes and Census ZIP Code Tabulation Areas (ZCTA). From this, you should be able to combine your two main data sources at the correct ZIP code level.

f. Consider whether the FEC data should be subsetted to a specific group of observations. You may need to collapse your data set so that it has the correct summaries for your analysis. For example, for your analysis, would it be more appropriate to examine the individual contributions data or to calculate a summary statistic to represent contributions across ZIP codes? The answer depends on your proposed analysis. Do not make your code data-dependent. For example, do not hardcode individual ZIP codes to have 5 digits instead of the ZIP + 4 format. Consider using a SAS function to do this instead.

g. Carry out the appropriate analysis (descriptive statistics, graphics, and hypothesis tests) to investigate your research questions. Additionally, consider using macros whenever it makes sense to reduce the amount of repeated code.

h. Write a paper that summarizes the programming and analysis for this project. The paper should be no more than 12 pages with an abstract, an introduction, main topics and results, a conclusion, and references. Include relevant discussion and snippets of code that represent all parts of the project as well as a description of the analysis. Include your results and a discussion of the analysis with the appropriate statistics and figures to support your work.

Lottery

The Mega Millions lottery (megamillions.com) is a multi-state number-matching game where a player buys a $2 ticket and picks five numbers and an additional number. Players can choose to pick their own numbers or use Easy Pick where the computer randomly picks the numbers for them. The odds and winnings for various combinations of numbers for the Mega Millions can be found at their website. Note that certain states require that awards are pari-mutuel payouts. This means that the prize amounts will vary depending on sales levels and number of winners. The Mega Millions lottery also offers ways for players to increase a non-jackpot prize by increasing their wager. For this project, we won't be taking into consideration how many people could have won and dividing of the jackpot or increased wager scenarios.

a. Write a macro that generates a random ticket for the Mega Millions. This consists of randomly selecting the five numbers (ranging 1 to 70) and an additional number (ranging 1 to 25). Verify on the Mega Millions website whether these are the current ranges for numbers. Each number should have an equal chance of being selected. Consider generating these numbers with a random number function such as RAND( ) and an appropriate statistical distribution. (See the online SAS Documentation for more details.) The five numbers cannot be duplicates, although the additional number is allowed to be a duplicate of any of the five numbers.

b. Write another macro that calls the macro from part a). This second macro should generate 200 tickets that are not duplicates of each other. (The five numbers on each ticket should be unique from ticket to ticket, although repeats for the additional number are OK.) This means that a ticket with the numbers 1,2,3,4,5 is the same as a ticket with the numbers 1,2,3,5,4. Your program should generate a new ticket and check it against the existing tickets so far, and then repeat this process until you have exactly 200 unique tickets.

c. Calculate your winnings based on the winnings scheme posted on the Mega Millions website and the most recent drawing. Once you've drawn the 200 unique tickets from parts a) and b), write another macro that passes in the winning numbers to identify whether any of the tickets are jackpot winners (all numbers match); any winnings; amount of money won; and number of matching numbers, not including the additional number.

d. Call your macros in a series of N simulations that picks 200 tickets each time. Start with 1,000 as your test case for number of simulations. Add programming to keep track of the following statistics for each of the 1,000 simulations: proportion of jackpot winners, proportion of any winnings, average amount of money won, and average number of matching numbers. For each of the four simulation statistics, create an appropriate graph to represent the distribution, and calculate the mean and standard deviation.

e. The graphics and statistics should be presented in HTML format that can be posted to a web page. You can only manipulate the web page formatting within your SAS code.

Loan Strategies

An amortization schedule is a table that lists the principal and interest charges, and the remaining balance for each payment across the life of a loan. Lenders use this type of schedule to determine monthly payments for most loans including mortgages. A portion of each payment is applied to the principal balance of the loan and the remainder of the payment goes toward interest. In the beginning of a loan, the interest portion of a payment is larger, and as the loan matures the portion allocated to the principal increases. The key formulas used to calculate an amortization schedule can be found easily on the internet.

Suppose that Isabel and Chris are very responsible first-time home buyers. They have a down payment of $120,000 which is 20% of a $600,000 home that they hope will help them avoid private mortgage insurance (PMI). PMI is insurance to cover the lender in case the buyer is not able to repay the loan. With their down payment, Isabel and Chris have committed to stick to a sales price of $600,000 or less. They are working with a loan officer who has presented them with two different options. Plan A is that they borrow $480,000 on a 30-year fixed rate loan at an interest rate of 6%. Plan B is that they pay four points (4% of the loan) to get a lower interest rate, and then they roll the point amount into the loan amount. This means that they borrow $499,200 on a 30-year fixed rate loan to get a smaller interest rate of 5.5%.

Isabel and Chris feel confused, so they call their parents and ask for advice. To make matters worse, their parents say that no matter what plan they choose they should add an additional $150 to their payment every month so that they can pay off their loan earlier. This gives Isabel and Chris two more scenarios. Plan C is that they borrow $480,000 on a 30-year fixed rate loan at an interest rate of 6%, and they add an additional $150 each month to their principal. Plan D is that they pay four points (4% of the loan) to get a lower interest rate of 5.5% rolling it into the loan amount totaling $499,200, and they add an additional $150 each month to their principal.

a. Write a SAS program that uses a DATA step to create an amortization schedule for plans A and B. The program should create the following variables for each observation: time period (by month), beginning balance, payment amount, interest amount for that payment, principal for that payment, and end balance.

b. Create an amortization schedule for the $150 pre-payment plans C and D. Make sure that for each schedule only the time periods where there is an actual balance get output to the data set. In other words, scenarios C and D will allow them to pay the loan off sooner than 30 years, so only print the applicable time points. In this way, they will know how early the loan will be paid off. Note that the end balance for the last time point is most likely somewhat less than the regular payment. In this case, adjust the last payment accordingly. Also, throughout the schedule, the payment amount variable should include the $150 extra that they will be applying toward their principal balance.

c. Once Isabel and Chris think that they have decided on their plan, they get another phone call from their parents. "Oh, by the way, don't forget that the amount of interest that you pay each year can be a deduction on your taxes. You might also want to review this before you decide on a plan," her father says. They thought they had it all figured out, but now they are back to square one. Use your programming from parts a) and b), to calculate the amount of interest paid annually across the total time frame of the loan. Because Isabel and Chris are already feeling overwhelmed, they would like to make a quick comparison across the four plans, and they do not want to see the entire amortization schedule for each one. Instead, they would like to have a summary with one row per plan (for a total of four observations) with a column for each year's interest. This means adding 30 variables to the data set that contains the total amount of interest paid for each of the 30 years (using the interest variable created in the amortization schedule). If there is no interest paid during the year for plans that are paid off early, then the interest should appear as zero.

d. They would also like to know the number of years until the loan is paid off. This can be calculated in the data set created in part c). Since the number of years will not always be an integer for plans C and D, it will be easier for them to understand if you create two variables, one for year (1 to 30) and one for month (1 to 12). Ultimately, the final summary data set should have variables for the plan (A, B, C, and D), payment amount, interest in each of the 30 years, year paid off, and month paid off.

e. Create a summary PDF report for Isabel and Chris to review. Incorporate the amortization schedules for the four plans created in parts a) and b) and the interest summary created in parts c) and d). Only print relevant variables and not extraneous information that may have been created along the way. Be sure to label and format the report appropriately.

Twitter Data

Twitter is a social networking service that was created in 2006. It allows users to send text-based messages known as tweets. Tweets are short messages that contain links to topics by the use of hashtags (such as #SAS) or to users with the @ symbol attached to a user name (such as @JSmith). In 2018 the limit for messages was increased from 140 to 280 characters. Tweets can be repeated by followers by re-tweeting (symbolized by RT followed by the original tweet.) Twitter topics are said to be trending if a hashtag for that topic is used at a high rate.

Social media data have recently become very popular in analytics. Examples of topics could be almost anything including popular events, releases of company services or products, breaking news, or even politics. Tweets can be analyzed for trends in the data as well as sentiment analysis based on individual words. For example, are topics or users trending on certain days or times? Are certain topics negative or positive in sentiment?

In order to analyze Twitter data, you must first capture the data using the Twitter API (Application Programming Interface) and then massage them into a usable form. The Twitter site contains many useful links for web developers that explain the sources and history of its data.

a.   Write a one-page research proposal to examine relationships in tweets that you find plausible and interesting. Make sure that you have identified enough variables to produce a well-thought-out data visualization through descriptive statistics and graphics. Some common social media analytic techniques that you should consider are who is influencing the conversation, sentiment of tweets, spikes in conversation over day or time, peak days or peak hours, graphics (such as bar charts and time trends), number of words per tweet, and keyword counts (including most frequent). Your analysis should include statistics and graphics both at the tweet level as described in part c) and also at the individual word level as described in part d).

b.   There are several SAS user group papers that provide macros for streaming Twitter data into SAS data sets. Research these user group papers to find code that will enable you to stream Twitter data on a topic of your choice into SAS. (Alternatively, you may also find Twitter data for predetermined topics already posted on the internet.)

c.   Create a data set containing information at the tweet level, which is one observation per tweet. Depending on your analytic plan, this might also include variables such as user name, language, location, time between tweets, day or time of the tweet, or a flag for re-tweets.

d.   Create another data set with data at the word level, one observation per word in the tweet. Words displayed as hashtags, user name references, and texting short-hand should also count as words. With these word counts, you should make a variable that flags hashtags (#) and user name references. Be careful to pull these data apart without respect to case. For example, #SAS should count the same as #sas when you are tallying up words.

e.   Users often use shorthand notation in their tweets. Research the internet for websites that have raw data files containing translations for emoticons and text acronyms so that they can be used to translate the shorthand into actual words. Combine these data with your Twitter data set at the word level replacing the shorthand with meaningful words while maintaining the intended structure of one observation per word. This is important when you are translating the emoticons and acronyms that might equate to more than one word. For example, LOL is three words, laugh out loud.

f.   Research the internet for websites that have raw data files containing negative and positive words. These words can be combined with the Twitter data to assign sentiment to a tweet, such as positive (+1), neutral (0), and negative (-1). You may want to sum these ranks to create a final sentiment score per tweet. To correctly define sentiment, make sure that you combine these data sets after the emoticons and texting acronyms have been replaced with words.

g.   Carry out the appropriate analysis (descriptive statistics, graphics, and hypothesis tests) to investigate your research questions. Additionally, consider using macros whenever it makes sense to reduce the amount of repeated code.

h. Write a paper that summarizes the programming and analysis for this project. The paper should be no more than 12 pages with an abstract, an introduction, main topics and results, a conclusion, and references. Include relevant discussion and snippets of code that represent all parts of the project as well as a description of the analysis. Include your results and a discussion of the analysis with the appropriate statistics and figures to support your work.

World Bank

The World Bank works internationally with the goal of reducing poverty. Their website (worldbank.org) includes a Data page that gives access to data sets about various indicators by country and indicator. The data sets can be downloaded to several file types including Microsoft Excel and CSV. The downloads include metadata files that provide information about the variables in the raw data file, the sources for the data, country code and region, income group, and special notes. Because these data are collected by country, they provide an opportunity to make comparisons between a country of interest and an aggregate group. This aggregate group could represent any comparison group of interest such as all other countries in the world, all other developed or developing countries, or all other countries within a certain continent.

a. Research the current World Bank indicators by the topic areas that are available.
b. Review the metadata information for a country and an aggregate group of your choice as well as indicators from at least three topic areas that you find interesting.
c. Based on your review, write a one-page research proposal that will compare certain indicators for your desired country to an aggregate group. State your country and time frame of interest. Describe the topic area data files that will provide the appropriate variables and statistics for your indicators of interest, and explain how you will define the aggregate group. Describe how you plan to combine and manipulate the data sources into an analyzable data set, and how you will deal with any missing data.
d. Write a SAS program that reads in the World Bank data as they relate to your research proposal. Manipulate your data sets so that you can combine them into one data set to be used for analysis.
e. Using your analytic data set, create a table that compares one indicator of your choice for your country of interest to an appropriate summary of the same indicator for the aggregate group. For example, create a table that examines by year the Urban Population Total (%) for the country versus the average Urban Population Total (%) in the aggregate group.
f. Create a graphic that corresponds to the statistics presented in your table. For example, create a series plot over time of the Urban Population Total (%) with a line for the country of interest and another line for the average Urban Population Total (%) in the aggregate group.

g.   Add a column to your table from part e) that presents the minimum and maximum across the aggregate countries for the same indicator. For example, calculate by year the minimum and maximum Urban Population Total (%) within the countries that represent the aggregate group. This new column will enable you to compare the data for the country of interest not only to the aggregate summary statistic calculated in part e), but also enable you to examine where the country falls among the range of the aggregate.

h.   Convert your code for the table and graphic into a macro. Add parameters to your macro that will enable you to specify a different country of interest and a different indicator. The macro should also allow for creating the appropriate summary statistics and graphic depending on the type of indicator that is being analyzed. You may also want to add parameters for other reporting features such as titles, footnotes, and labels. Use this macro to create a report for your country and indicators of interest. Then choose another country, review the metadata information to ensure that the report will be valid for this country, and run the macro again to create a new report.

Toxic Chemicals

The United States Environmental Protection Agency (EPA) provides a toxic release inventory (TRI) program that tracks potentially hazardous substances in many communities. There are hundreds of chemicals that have been determined to be toxic, and certain industries that use these chemicals must report their use to the EPA. The Customized Search feature found on the Envirofacts TRI search website, found at epa.gov, enables you to build a customized data set by following basic steps to identify subjects, tables, and variables of interest for your desired year, location, facility, or chemical. The data element search tool is a helpful link that specifies all the variables available for TRI data sets. The TRI data also contain latitude and longitude, which can be used to investigate distance to any location.

a.   Research the current TRI data that are available by subject area.

b.   Review the information available from at least three different subject areas that you find interesting.

c.   Based on your review, write a one-page research proposal that will examine relationships in the TRI data for a year, location, facility, or chemical of interest that includes a focus on distance. Describe the subject area data files that will support your questions of interest, the appropriate variables, and statistics for your research questions. Describe how you plan to combine and manipulate the data sources into an analyzable data set, and how you will deal with any missing data.

d.   Write a SAS program that reads in the TRI data as they relate to your research proposal. Manipulate your data sets so that you can combine them into one data set to be used for analysis.

e. Incorporate distance into your analysis for a location of interest such as your home, university, or workplace. Calculate distance using the latitude and longitude of a facility and your place of interest. There are many websites that can provide you with a latitude and longitude for an address or ZIP code. You can use the GEODIST function in SAS to calculate the distance between two latitude and longitude points.

f. Carry out the appropriate analysis (descriptive statistics, graphics, and hypothesis tests) to investigate your research questions. Additionally, consider using macros whenever it makes sense to reduce the amount of repeated code.

g. Write a paper that summarizes the programming and analysis for this project. The paper should be no more than 12 pages with an abstract, an introduction, main topics and results, a conclusion, and references. Include relevant discussion and snippets of code that represent all parts of the project as well as a description of the analysis. Include your results and a discussion of the analysis with the appropriate statistics and figures to support your work.

SELECTED SOLUTIONS

Chapter 1—Getting Started Using SAS Software

1. D
3. A
5. C
7. C
9. B
11. A
13. B
15. B

17. The layout of this code is disorganized, but it will not cause an error. Individual SAS statements can continue across multiple lines as long as there are no breaks in the words, and multiple SAS statements can be written on the same line. Each statement in this program ends appropriately with a semicolon.

    ```
    PROC PRINT DATA = new;
    RUN;
    ```

19. It would be better to store the annual salary as a numeric variable so that it can be used in calculations, such as the mean salary of employees.

21. When SAS creates a SAS data set, it automatically stores information about the data set itself such as the name and date/time it was created. SAS also stores information about the variables such as type (numeric or character) and length. This is called the descriptor portion of the data set.

23. By default, the DATA step automatically processes all observations in a data set starting with the first observation. SAS runs through the entire DATA step once for each observation.

25. Global statements can appear anywhere in your program and do not belong to DATA or PROC steps. RUN and OPTIONS are examples of global statements.

27. *Hint:* Use the color coding in the editor to help you catch any typos that might occur accidentally when you type in the DATA step.

28. *Hint:* You may be able to use a Find feature in your SAS environment to help find things in your SAS log.

29. *Hint:* In the log, the notes, warnings, and errors are color coded and identified by their names. There are two problems that need to be fixed in this program.

Chapter 2—Accessing Your Data

1. D
3. A
5. C
7. D
9. C
11. C
13. B
15. B
17. A
19. C
21. C
23. C
25. B

27. When using LIBNAME statements, you only have to define the location once and can then refer to the libref throughout the program. LIBNAME statements come in handy when pointing to the same location repeatedly within a program. When using direct referencing, you refer to the path and name of the data set directly in the DATA or PROC step. Direct referencing may save programming time when referencing many different paths within one program.

29. Internal raw data are typed directly into a DATA step inside the SAS program. You might choose to use internal raw data if you have a small number of observations and variables. Another time you might choose to use internal raw data might be with a small test data set, or data that are used to carry out a simple calculation. External raw data are stored in a data file separate from your program. External data files are appropriate for large amounts of data, and are typical of what you might be given by a client.

31. Missing data indicated by a space, character data with embedded spaces (assuming that an ampersand modifier is not used in the INPUT statement), character data longer than eight characters (assuming that a LENGTH or INFORMAT statement is not used in the DATA step), nonstandard numeric data, and data that are not separated by a delimiter such as a space are all examples of data that cannot be read using list input.

33. Using a LENGTH statement tells SAS to create a variable with a designated length that could accommodate longer city names in this case. However, some of the city names for this data set have embedded blanks so list input will not read the data correctly. Modified list input will not work to read in the city names correctly because the City variable is separated from Name1 by only one space.

35. One possible answer is.

    ```
    INPUT Brand $ 1-18 Qty Amount DOLLAR6.2;
    ```

37. If your data file uses a space as the delimiter, then using the colon modifier will not allow you to read embedded blanks because SAS interprets a space as the end of the data value. If your data file uses a different delimiter, such as a comma, then embedded blanks would not cause problems for the colon modifier.

39. ```
    INPUT ID Group $ @@;
    IF Group = 'B' THEN DELETE;
    ```

41. TRUNCOVER is used for column or formatted input when your data set has variables at the end of the record that may vary in length. With the TRUNCOVER option, if the record ends in the middle of a column range or format for the variable, then SAS will just take whatever is there instead of assigning the variable a missing value. MISSOVER also deals with records that vary in length, but assigns missing values to variables with missing data at the end of the record. The MISSOVER and TRUNCOVER options prevent SAS from being forced to the next line in search of data for these missing or incomplete fields.

43. One possible answer is.

    ```
    INFILE 'c:\MyRawData\Records.csv' DLM = ',' MISSOVER;
    ```

44. *Hint:* Examine the type of delimiter used in this file.

45. *Hint:* Remember to tell SAS which variables are character.
    ```

46. *Hint:* List input alone will not work for this raw data file because of missing data and embedded spaces in names of breeds.

47. *Hint:* Pay attention to missing data and be careful to designate character data correctly.

48. *Hint:* Consider informats for any nonstandard numeric data. You may also need to position the pointer before reading values for some variables.

49. *Hint:* Pay attention to the varying columns and missing values for the last three variables.

50. *Hint:* Because some of the data values contain spaces, you cannot read the data with simple list input. Be careful reading the data values for prominence which vary in length at the end of each record.

51. *Hint:* For the rows of data for students, think about how to tell SAS to skip a line and remove the observation.

52. *Hint:* Consider the layout of the raw data file and what options might be required to read this data set.

53. *Hint:* Examine how missing values are recorded in the raw data file. Also pay attention to the lengths of the character variables.

54. *Hint:* Notice that in the Microsoft Excel file there are no variable names. If you have a mixture of 32-bit and 64-bit applications installed on your computer, then you may not be able to use PROC IMPORT to read Excel files.

55. *Hint:* Think about how SAS may need to move the pointer depending on if the data will be kept in the data set or deleted. What will tell SAS to stay on the line of data through multiple iterations of the DATA step?

56. *Hint:* Viewing the raw data file in a simple editor such as WordPad will enable you to see the original format of the file. Opening the file in Microsoft Excel will incorrectly display the raw data. Missing values in the beginning of a data file may cause PROC IMPORT to read the data incorrectly. In the final SAS data set, the survey number variable should be character and all other variables should be numeric.

57. *Hint:* The variable names in the header row cannot be read in when simultaneously reading in a section of data from the middle of the data set.

Chapter 3—Working with Your Data

1. B
3. B
5. B
7. C
9. A
11. C
13. A
15. C
17. B
19. B
21. A

23. When the original data set needs to be preserved, it is not a good idea to overwrite it by using the same data set name in the DATA and SET statements. Once you have overwritten a data set, if you make a mistake in your coding, or subset the data incorrectly, it might be difficult to get the original data set back. For this reason, it is a good idea to keep backup copies of important data sets.

25. When referring to missing numeric data, you should not include quotation marks around the period. Doing this will create a character variable X with a length of 1 and a value of a period (.) instead of a numeric missing value.

27. Yes. If your data set might have inconsistencies in capitalization, such as yes, Yes, and YES, then forcing the values to be all uppercase (or lowercase or mixed case) will simplify your program. For example, IF UPCASE(Result) = 'YES'; will catch all possible scenarios.

29. There are four changes that can be made. First, add a DO statement to group smokers and non-smokers to reduce repetitive code. Second, use IF-THEN/ELSE statements so that SAS can stop checking once the condition is met. Third, due to the hierarchical nature of the risk groups and the IF-THEN/ELSE statements, the conditions should be arranged so that the highest risk group comes first. Fourth, add ELSE statements to classify an unknown risk group.

```
** For smokers;
IF Smoke > 0 THEN DO;
   ** Assign the higher risk groups first;
   IF Sbp >= 140 OR Dbp >= 90
```

```
                    THEN Risk = 'Severe';
           ELSE IF 120 <= Sbp < 140 OR 80 <= Dbp < 90
                    THEN Risk = 'High';
           ELSE IF 0 < Sbp < 120 AND 0 < Dbp < 80
                    THEN Risk = 'Medium';
           ELSE Risk = 'Unk';
   END;

   ** For non-smokers;
   ELSE IF Smoke = 0 THEN DO;
     IF Sbp >= 140 OR Dbp >= 90
                    THEN Risk = 'High';
           ELSE IF 120 <= Sbp < 140 OR 80 <= Dbp < 90
                    THEN Risk = 'Medium';
           ELSE IF 0 < Sbp < 120 AND 0 < Dbp < 80
                    THEN Risk = 'Low';
           ELSE Risk = 'Unk';
   END;

   ** Assign unknown for any observations with a missing
      value for Smoke;
   ELSE Risk = 'Unk';
```

31. When using an ELSE statement without an IF condition, the action will be performed for all observations that did not meet the condition specified in the previous IF-THEN/ELSE statements. This means that you should be confident that all remaining observations will fit into this final category, and that you did not unintentionally miss a condition that should have been specified with another IF-THEN/ELSE statement.

33. SAS executes statements in the DATA step in the order in which they appear. Therefore, it will output the observations to the SAS data set called FEMALEHEIGHT before it carries out the calculation for the HeightCM variable. The solution would be to swap the statements so that the calculation comes before the OUTPUT statement. Alternatively, you could use a subsetting IF statement instead of an OUTPUT statement. A subsetting IF statement would not override the implied OUTPUT statement at the end of the DATA step.

35. A DO statement executes a DO group once for each observation that meets the condition specified by the DO statement. An iterative DO statement executes a DO group repeatedly for each observation incrementing a counter with each execution.

37. A date format is used to present the data in the output in a more readable form than the number of days since January 1, 1960. Note that a date format does not actually change the values of the data in the SAS data set.

39. Differences: The RETAIN statement has a keyword; a sum statement does not have any keywords. With a RETAIN statement, you can specify the initial value; with a sum statement you cannot. A RETAIN statement only retains a value from the preceding iteration of a DATA step; a sum statement retains the value and adds it to another data value. RETAIN can be used with character or numeric data while sum can only be used with numeric data. Similarities: Both the RETAIN and sum statements preserve a value from the previous iteration of the DATA step. Both RETAIN and sum should be used to create new variables rather than modify existing variables.

41. *Hint:* Consider using a loop to calculate the number of weeks to spend $1,000 on gasoline.

42. *Hint:* Be careful how the totals are calculated on records with missing data.

43. *Hint:* Consider using functions to facilitate the creation of new variables. In addition, DO statements will help with grouping observations with similar conditions.

44. *Hint:* IF-THEN/ELSE statements will result in less code for the phone number listing.

45. *Hint:* You may need to create a new variable to assist in tracking when the winning team name changes as you step through the data set.

46. *Hint:* Consider the use of arrays and range lists to shorten your program. Pay attention to how you specify the existing variable names in the DATA step.

47. *Hint:* You will need to tell SAS to preserve information across iterations of the DATA step.

48. *Hint:* The raw data file uses a delimiter other than spaces. Think about the order of events when recoding the data. Arrays and iterative DO statements of various sizes can help with the many groupings and calculations.

Chapter 4—Sorting, Printing, and Summarizing Your Data

1. B
3. D
5. B
7. D
9. D

11. B

13. A

15. C

17. C

19. B

21. B

23. SAS prints titles at the top of each page of the output. SAS prints labels in place of the variable names. Labels can be stored with the data set while titles cannot.

25. Using the OUT= option will create a new data set with the sorted data. If you were using a WHERE statement in the PROC SORT to subset the data, it would be wise to include an OUT= option to create a new data set and prevent overwriting the original data set. However, if you do not need to preserve the original data set, then it would be okay to skip the OUT= option in PROC SORT, which would save disk space by not creating a new data set.

27. An informat tells SAS how to read raw data. A format tells SAS how to display data.

29. You can create a user-defined format and then use it in a procedure instead of creating a new character variable in a DATA step. This saves the storage space of another variable in your data set. In addition, the user-defined format can be used anywhere in the program, even with other data sets that code gender in the same way.

31. When using the CLASS statement with PROC MEANS, the data do not have to be sorted first. In order to use the BY statement, the data must be sorted first. The resulting output with the CLASS statement is also more compact, which could be useful when providing summaries of the data.

33. Using the OUTPUT statement in PROC MEANS will create a data set. You can generate a summary report without an OUTPUT statement. Unless you need to merge the summary statistics with another data set, the results without an OUTPUT statement will most likely be enough.

35. PROC REPORT has the ability to create computed variables. PROC REPORT can create detail reports with one row per observation and summary reports. PROC TABULATE only creates summary reports. PROC TABULATE can use character variables only as headers.

37. *Hint*: Think about how SAS sorts numerals that are contained in character data.

38. *Hint*: Consider using IF-THEN/ELSE statements to distinguish between the two layout patterns.

39. *Hint*: Find a way to group the month data into quarters without using IF-THEN statements in a DATA step.

40. *Hint*: Use optional statements to keep the report of potential errors looking clean.

41. *Hint*: Use the structure of this data set, with one categorical variable to describe Topping and one continuous variable to describe Rating, to help you choose which SAS statements to use for the reports.

42. *Hint*: The variable labels will tell you which code corresponds to Yes and No for the VegMeal variable. Experiment with the various procedures in this chapter to find which ones will work best for parts d) and e).

43. *Hint*: Consider using a subsetting statement within the procedures to select the observations of interest.

44. *Hint*: Use a procedure to calculate new variables without the use of a DATA step.

Chapter 5 — Enhancing Your Output with ODS

1. B
3. D
5. C
7. D
9. A
11. C
13. A
15. D

17. The STYLE= option in an ODS statement specifies a style template for the overall presentation of the output. SAS has many built-in style templates. You can also create your own templates using PROC TEMPLATE. In comparison, the STYLE= option for PROC PRINT allows you to change specific features of your output, such as the font or color of cells and table headers, without having to modify an entire template.

19. Using a STYLE= option in the PROC TABULATE statement will apply the style to all of the data cells. Using a STYLE= option in the TABLE statement will apply the style to specific cells, and will override any style defined by the PROC TABULATE statement.

21. When you set a style attribute equal to a user-defined format, also known as trafficlighting, different styles are assigned to different data values. When you set a style attribute equal to a specific value, you are assigning the same style to all cells.

23. ODS statements are global, which means that they can go anywhere in the program. But their placement really depends on which ODS statement you use. For example, the ODS PDF statement can open a PDF destination and write to a file. All printable results produced between the opening and closing of the PDF destination will be included in the output. So in this case, it is important to put all relevant procedures in the middle. The ODS OUTPUT statement is a stand-alone statement that opens a data set destination in order to capture the specified object from the next procedure that runs. In this case, it is important that the ODS OUTPUT statement be placed before or inside the procedure that produces the output you wish to capture.

24. *Hint*: Use ODS statements and options to turn certain portions of the output into data and to control page breaks.

25. *Hint*: Be sure to put your ODS statements where they will capture the results of both procedures. In the SAS windowing environment, once all the destinations are closed, you may want to reopen the default destination, or exit SAS to reset the destination.

26. *Hint*: Consider using a WHERE statement to select the desired applicants. The various styles for shading may require more than one VAR statement. In the SAS windowing environment, once all the destinations are closed, you may want to reopen the default destination, or exit SAS to reset the destination.

27. *Hint*: Review the codes specified in the variable labels in the SAS data set. Consider reformatting the data values with meaningful code descriptions so that they will appear cleaner in the output. Find an ODS statement option that will eliminate default titles for each table.

28. *Hint*: The data have already been analyzed and consolidated and just need to be formatted for presentation.

29. *Hint*: The best procedures to carry out each task may vary.

Chapter 6—Modifying and Combining SAS Data Sets

1. D
3. D
5. B
7. D
9. C
11. C
13. C
15. A
17. D

19. If your data are not sorted and do not need to be sorted, then stacking requires fewer steps than interleaving. You would also want to stack if the goal is to maintain the original order of the observations in the data sets. If your data need to be sorted, then it may be more efficient to stack the data sets and then sort the combined data. Interleaving would require sorting each data set separately, which requires longer code and may waste computer resources for large data sets.

21. When doing a one-to-many merge, one of the data sets must have unique values of the BY variables. If you get this message in the log, then you need to remove the duplicate observations from one of the data sets before doing the merge. You can check for duplicates in a data set using PROC SORT with the NODUPKEY option. This will remove all observations from the data set that have duplicate values of the BY variables. To see which observations are removed, use the DUPOUT= option to store the duplicates in a separate data set. This method of removing duplicates is good if you don't care which of the duplicate observations are saved. If some of the other, non-BY, variables in the data set have different values, then you may want more control over which observations are kept. In this case, careful sorting and using the FIRST. and LAST. automatic variables in a DATA step may be useful.

23. Using PROC SQL allows you to combine data in one step. The use of PROC SORT for a merge can be avoided because PROC SQL creates a Cartesian product. Additionally, PROC SQL does not require the key matching variables to have the same name while merging in a DATA step does. Adding summary statistics to a data set can be accomplished in the same PROC SQL step with a summary function in the SELECT clause, and possibly a GROUP BY clause, which avoids an additional procedure such as PROC MEANS.

25. Using the WHERE= option in the SET statement will control what observations are read in. This could result in improved processing time when reading a subset of data from a large data set. Using the WHERE= option in the DATA statement will control what observations are written to the data set.

27. *Hint*: Carefully inspect the variable names and labels for each data set. Consider tracking the data set source in order to create the country name variable.

28. *Hint*: Think about which variables are common to both data sets even though they may not have the same variable names.

29. *Hint*: For part b), consider which variables you want to keep from the old data set, which variable will define the new variable names, and which variable contains the data values. Be sure to sort the data before using a BY statement in a subsequent DATA or PROC step.

30. *Hint*: Think about procedures that can calculate medians and how you could combine those results with a SAS data set.

31. *Hint*: The FIRST. and LAST. variables are created when you use a BY statement in a DATA step, even in a merge. Use FIRST. or LAST. to reset the counter variable.

32. *Hint*: You may need more than one DATA step to combine the data and various statistics. You may also need to create more than one data set when working with PROC SQL.

33. *Hint*: Consider which procedures you can use to count the number of older and younger siblings. Use FIRST. and LAST. to find the youngest and oldest siblings.

34. *Hint*: Think about the best way to combine the two original data sets without creating a lot of missing data values. Back up the original FRIENDS data set using system commands.

Chapter 7—Writing Flexible Code with the SAS Macro Facility

1. B
3. A
5. B
7. C

9. A

11. A

13. If your program uses the same variable or text value many times, then using a macro variable will enable you to update the program more easily if you ever need to change the variable or text. You can assign a value to the macro variable at the beginning of the program. Each macro variable reference throughout the program will be replaced with its value after macro resolution.

15. The macro processor resolves macro references inside double quotation marks, but not inside single quotation marks. In this example, using double quotation marks will allow the automatic macro variable &SYSDAY to resolve to the day of the week.

17. A macro variable holds a single piece of text. When the program is submitted, the text will be substituted for the macro variable name anywhere the name appears in the program. A macro consists of a block of code. The statements inside the macro can be executed any number of times by simply invoking the macro. Macros can contain macro variables and can use complex logic such as %IF-%THEN/%ELSE for added flexibility.

19. A parameter is a macro variable that is defined when you invoke a macro and the value of the parameter gets passed to the macro. Using parameters in macros greatly increases their flexibility by allowing you to change what the macro does based on the parameter's value.

21. *Hint:* Be sure to make the necessary changes to the TABLES, WHERE, and TITLE statements.

22. *Hint:* For part b) consider using macro statements that will control which standard SAS statements will be resolved by the macro processor. Remember you are writing a program that writes a program.

23. *Hint:* Consider how best to name the variables and data sets created in part c) so that they will combine correctly in part d). For part f) consider using macro programming that allows you to iterate through the years.

24. *Hint:* Consider using a procedure to calculate the average, and creating data-driven macro variables for the footnote.

25. *Hint:* Using conditional logic within the macro will enable you to write one macro that will work for all property types for part c). For part d), you will need to save the means for each of the property types in separate data sets, and then combine them together outside the macro.

26. *Hint*: Be careful to type the program into the editor *exactly as written*.

Chapter 8—Visualizing Your Data

1. D
3. A
5. B
7. C
9. B
11. D
13. C
15. C

17. No, SAS would not make this graph. These plot types are incompatible because VBAR is typically used for categorical data while HISTOGRAM is designed for use with continuous data. In this case, SAS would return an error message.

19. For series plots, SAS connects the points in the order in which they appear in the data set, which is not necessarily the correct order of the X axis. Sorting the data by the X variable will fix this problem.

21. The SIZE= attribute can be used to specify the font size of a label or marker. The THICKNESS= attribute is used to specify the width of a line. Both attributes specify numbers with a choice of units (CM, IN, MM, PCT, PT, or PX).

23. *Hint:* You can create the histograms for all the continents in one SGPLOT, and similarly for the box plots.

24. *Hint:* Create a customized format to label missing values. Create a new data set for the paneled graph so that there is one observation for each survey question for each subject.

25. *Hint:* Use a DATA step to create a variable that can be plotted on the graph to identify the county with the largest number of patents.

26. *Hint:* This exercise will produce only one graphic. Create a variable for average magnitude that is combined with the original data set.

27. *Hint:* For part c), create two regression plots with one REG statement by selecting the appropriate option.

28. *Hint:* The data will need some summarization before being plotted. To insert text inside the plot area for part e), you will need to add some new variables to the data set for the text and the placement of the text on the plot. These new variables will have missing values for all but two observations, and they will need to be specified in an additional plot statement.

Chapter 9—Using Basic Statistical Procedures

1. B
3. B
5. C
7. C
9. C
11. D
13. A
15. D

17. This data set has the differences already calculated, so you could carry out this test by treating the data like a one-sample *t* test for the mean difference. In this case, you could use PROC UNIVARIATE, MEANS, or TTEST with only a VAR statement to accomplish a simple test of any difference. In PROC TTEST, you would not use the PAIRED statement for this data set because there is only one variable.

19. To test an association between two categorical variables, you would use PROC FREQ with a CHISQ option in the TABLE statement.

21. In a correlation matrix, the diagonal represents a comparison of a variable with itself. Because these correlations are a perfect relationship, a scatter plot would be uninformative. A histogram is used instead of a scatter plot to provide univariate information about the distribution of the variable.

23. The MEANS statement will calculate the means of the dependent variable (Wds) for each level of the main effect (Mag). With the SCHEFFE option this statement will also calculate Scheffe's multiple comparisons of group means.

24. *Hint:* Think of a way to group the countries without using a DATA step. Use a CLASS statement to tell SAS to compute the descriptive statistics by United States versus non-United States.

25. *Hint:* Which procedure will help you flip the layout of the data set so that you can conduct the correct hypothesis tests on plaque? Using the appropriate BY and/or CLASS statements will allow you to carry out the requested hypothesis tests with one procedure for each part.

26. *Hint:* The code for these tests can be written with one PROC step.

27. *Hint:* Using PROC CONTENTS or viewing the data set interactively will help you identify the order of the variables. You do not need a DATA step to limit an analysis to certain observations.

28. *Hint:* Use a function to perform the base 10 log transformation. Use an ODS TRACE statement to examine the output objects for the analysis.

29. *Hint:* Consider modifying the layout of the data set so that you can conduct the appropriate hypothesis tests on route time for the three plans.

Chapter 10—Exporting Your Data

1. A
3. D
5. A
7. A
9. B

11. When you export a data file with PROC EXPORT, there is specific syntax and options that allow you to create an export file. With the DATA step, you must specify every aspect of the data file. The DATA step is more work, but it is also more flexible than the EXPORT procedure. For example, the DATA step allows the use of pointer controls, line controls, and formats. With the EXPORT procedure each observation will be on a single row using one delimiter to separate the data values.

13. *Hint:* Make sure that the character data with embedded commas are enclosed in double quotation marks.

14. *Hint:* Detailed information about the continent names and years appears in the variable labels. To create this file, you may need multiple PROC steps, but you do not need multiple DATA steps.

15. *Hint:* Be sure to check the variable types and formats. Consider using different PUT statements depending on the value for appointment date. Think about how you can display just the first letter of a name without creating a new variable.

16. *Hint:* Look for a system option to display missing numeric data as blanks.

Chapter 11—Debugging Your SAS Programs

1. A
3. A
5. D
7. D
9. C
11. A
13. B
15. D
17. D
19. C

21. To fix this program, you need to place a semicolon at the end of the INPUT statement. The first error message indicates that SAS does not understand that the data values are data. The second error message claims that there is no DATALINES or INFILE statement. Without the semicolon, the DATALINES keyword becomes a variable name in the INPUT statement. This results in no DATALINES statement, and SAS tries to interpret the actual data values as some sort of SAS statement. The note tells you that SAS will not run this program due to the errors that it has encountered. The warning lets you know that your data set has no observations, which may be an indication that something is wrong. It also states that there are four variables when there should have been only three.

23. SAS displays each statement that you submit in the log along with a line number. The (line):(column) information in the log refers to that line number and column within the line. This information is important because it tells you where to look in your code to find potential problems.

25. The issue with this DATA step is that there is no variable D in the NEW data set. The first note indicates that the variable D cannot be found. After this note SAS will initialize D and continue to execute, but the variable D will have missing values for all observations. The second note tells you that some values of the variable Total, as identified at line three of the log, will have missing values. Three observations in this data set will have this result. The reference 3:21 pinpoints exactly where the missing values were generated. In this case, it was the plus sign between the variables C and D (line 3 column 21).

27. *Hint:* Consider using different INPUT statements depending on whether the record includes an address or a name and amount.

28. *Hint:* Use an informat modifier to suppress the invalid-data notes for date of birth.

29. *Hint:* There are six mistakes in the code.

30. *Hint:* There are five mistakes in the code.

31. *Hint:* Examine the data values along with the variable types and attributes because there are a number of issues with the data sets that may cause problems. You cannot change the type of a variable directly. Instead, consider renaming variables and then reusing the original variable name where appropriate.

Ready to take your SAS® and JMP® skills up a notch?

Be among the first to know about new books, special events, and exclusive discounts.
support.sas.com/newbooks

Share your expertise. Write a book with SAS.
support.sas.com/publish

sas.com/books
for additional books and resources.

THE POWER TO KNOW.

Made in the USA
Columbia, SC
03 November 2022

70418062R00083